ReadyGEN®

SO-CFO-694

GRADE 2

Reader's and Writer's Journal
TEACHER'S GUIDE

PEARSON

Glenview, Illinois • Boston, Massachusetts • Chandler, Arizona • Hoboken, New Jersey

PEARSON

ISBN-13: 978-0-328-85164-5
ISBN-10: 0-328-85164-7

6 17

Table of Contents

Name _____

Short Vowels

si**ng** do**ck** ki**ng** clo**ck** si**nk**

Say the word for each picture. **Write a, e, i, o,** or **u** to finish each word. Then **circle** the word that completes each sentence.

1. 2. 3. 4.

b**a**nk r**i**ng s**o**ck n**e**ck

5. 6. 7. 8.

d**u**ck tr**u**ck w**i**ng r**o**ck

9. Jan can _____ the ball. (kick) pocket picnic

10. Tim gives Jan a _____. sing (ring) nose

Children apply grade-level phonics and word analysis skills.

Name _____

DIRECTIONS Write sentences using the words below.

shade　　plastic　　spade　　shadow

Responses should show contextual understanding of the words.

Write in Response to Reading

DIRECTIONS Reread p. 4 of _Trouble at the Sandbox_. Who was making a river for the volcano? Use text evidence to support your answer.

The text says Izzy was making the river.

Children demonstrate contextual understanding of Benchmark Vocabulary. Children read text closely and use text evidence in their written answers.

DIRECTIONS Reread pp. 2–5 of *Trouble at the Sandbox*. Write a paragraph about how Theo might respond to a classmate other than Izzy or Josh. Use key details from the text to help you.

Responses should use evidence from the text

including that Theo was helpful and didn't mind

sharing.

Conventions

Identify Nouns Circle the nouns in the sentences below.

1. The grass was wet.
2. The sandbox is full of fresh sand.
3. Izzy wanted to dig a tunnel!
4. The girl peered through the door.
5. My classmate built a bridge during recess.

Children write routinely for a range of tasks, purposes, and audiences. Children practice various conventions of standard English.

Name _____

DIRECTIONS Write sentences using the words below.

scared carrying upset

Responses should show
contextual understanding of the
words.

DIRECTIONS Reread p. 7 of *Trouble at the Sandbox*. Write a sentence that tells why Josh looked like he was going to cry. Use examples from the text to support your answer.

The text says a big boy got the
truck from Josh, which was why
Josh was about to cry.

Children demonstrate contextual understanding of Benchmark Vocabulary. Children read text closely and use text evidence in their written answers.

Name _____

DIRECTIONS Using text evidence, answer the following questions about pp. 6–8 of *Trouble at the Sandbox*.

1. What happens first on p. 6?

Theo asks if they want to play.

2. What happens next?

The big boy laughs in a mean way.

3. On p. 7, what happens after Josh tells the older boys that they need the trucks?

The big boy says he doesn't care.

4. List two events that take place on p. 8.

Responses might include the boys take the

trucks, and Theo tells a teacher.

Children analyze and respond to literary and informational text.

DIRECTIONS Create a classmate that will interact with the big boys. Write a paragraph that explains how the big boys would respond to that classmate. How would that classmate interact with the big boys? Use details from pp. 6–8 of *Trouble at the Sandbox* to support your paragraph.

Responses may indicate that the classmate tries to stop the boys, but they still take the toys.

Conventions

Capitalize Proper Nouns Circle the proper nouns that should be capitalized.

1. (monica) lives in a city called (portland).
2. (theo) enjoys playing in the sandbox.
3. They went to tell Ms. (lee) everything that happened.
4. (izzy) was upset because the older boys were mean to them.
5. The big boy laughed at Theo and (josh).

Children write routinely for a range of tasks, purposes, and audiences. Children practice various conventions of standard English.

Name _____

DIRECTIONS Write sentences using the words below.

breath calm searched

Responses should show contextual understanding of the words.

Write in
Response to
Reading

DIRECTIONS Reread p. 10 of *Trouble at the Sandbox*. How does Theo feel about Ms. Lee? How do you know? Use evidence from the text to support your answer.

Responses should use evidence from the text including that Theo thinks Ms. Lee is kind.

Children demonstrate contextual understanding of Benchmark Vocabulary. Children read text closely and use text evidence in their written answers.

The Hunt for Amelia's Ring

"Janine, have you seen my ring?" Amelia asked.

Janine *had* seen her sister's ring. She had tried it on, but it was a little big, so she took it off . . . but where did she put it? Janine couldn't remember!

When she told her sister the truth, Amelia was upset. Janine had to find that ring! She crawled under tables, peeked inside dresser drawers, looked behind the couch, and opened every cabinet. Finally, she gave up and went outside to sit on the front steps.

Her neighbor, Mrs. Kim, came up the steps "I find it useful to retrace my steps when I can't find something," Mrs. Kim said.

Janine thought and thought. First, she had done homework, and then she had eaten a snack. Then . . . aha! She remembered!

Janine helped carry Mrs. Kim's groceries. Then she ran to her apartment and went to the kitchen windowsill. There it was! The ring was right where Janine had left it when she helped water Mom's plants. Janine ran to give it to Amelia. She had learned her lesson about taking what wasn't hers. She also learned that two heads are better than one when there is a mystery to solve!

Children read text closely to determine what the text says.

Name _____

Look for Clues
Underline the text that tells how Mrs. Kim helped Janine.

Look for Clues: Extend Your Ideas
What did Janine do once Mrs. Kim gave her that tip?

She retraced her steps.

Ask Questions
Write a question that you might ask someone who has lost something. **Responses will vary.**

Example: How do you feel?

Ask Questions: Extend Your Ideas
Ask a question that you might follow up with if the person found the lost item. **Responses will vary.**

Example: Are you glad?

Make Your Case
Underline the text that tells how Amelia reacted to Janine losing her ring. Then underline the text that tells how Janine reacted when she found the ring.

Make Your Case: Extend Your Ideas
Identify one lesson Janine learned. Write the lesson on a sheet of paper. **not to take things that are not hers**

Children read text closely to determine what the text says.

Name _____

DIRECTIONS You will create a character who will be a friend of Theo's. Use the graphic organizer to help you list your character's physical traits, thoughts, and word choices. Write a paragraph using the information from the web. Be sure to include Theo's point of view of the character. On a separate piece of paper, draw a picture of the character to illustrate your description.

Responses will vary but the paragraph should reflect the information in the web and Theo's point of view.

Conventions

Plural Nouns Underline the plural nouns.

1. day	<u>farmers</u>	<u>boots</u>	spider	<u>animals</u>
2. sand	boy	teacher	<u>trucks</u>	<u>friends</u>
3. box	<u>volcanoes</u>	<u>cats</u>	school	<u>arms</u>
4. cup	keyboard	<u>books</u>	computer	mouse

Children write routinely for a range of tasks, purposes, and audiences. Children practice various conventions of standard English.

Name _____

DIRECTIONS Write sentences using the words below.

shrugged tipped awesome sank

Responses should show contextual understanding of the words.

> Write in
> Response to
> Reading

DIRECTIONS Reread p. 14 of *Trouble at the Sandbox*. How does Theo feel when he turns around and sees that the big boy is behind him again? Use examples from the text to support your answer.

The text says that Theo looked up and his heart sank.

Children demonstrate contextual understanding of Benchmark Vocabulary. Children read text closely and use text evidence in their written answers.

DIRECTIONS Using evidence from the text, answer the following questions about pp. 12–14 of *Trouble at the Sandbox*.

I. List three events that happened on pp. 12–14.

Responses will vary but may include: The bell rang; the next day, the trucks were there; the big boys returned.

2. How does Izzy feel when she sees the volcano?

Izzy is happy because she says, "Awesome."

3. What does Izzy do after Josh fills the truck with water?

She helps Theo fill the moat.

Children analyze and respond to literary and informational text.

Name _____

DIRECTIONS Choose a character from *Trouble at the Sandbox* and create a new character. Imagine an event that your new character and the character from the text will have different points of view about. Then write a narrative using dialogue that shows these differing points of view.

Responses should include a character from the text and one new character. They have differing points of view about an event.

Conventions

Irregular Plural Nouns Cross out the irregular plural nouns.

1. ~~children~~	birds	~~sheep~~	~~mice~~	bugs
2. ~~teeth~~	buses	~~people~~	hats	dogs
3. cups	~~men~~	rabbits	~~loaves~~	desks
4. cows	~~geese~~	crows	~~wolves~~	gerbils

 Children write routinely for a range of tasks, purposes, and audiences. Children practice various conventions of standard English.

Benchmark Vocabulary

DIRECTIONS Write sentences using the words below.

bravely background

Responses should show contextual understanding of

the words.

Write in Response to Reading

DIRECTIONS Reread p. 16 of *Trouble at the Sandbox*. How does Ms. Lee's point of view change? Why? Use evidence from the text to support your answer.

Ms. Lee is mad until she comes out of the staff room.

She seems to know where the trucks are.

Children demonstrate contextual understanding of Benchmark Vocabulary. Children read text closely and use text evidence in their written answers.

Name _____

DIRECTIONS Using evidence from pp. 15–18 of *Trouble at the Sandbox,* follow the directions below.

1. On the lines below, write the names of two characters. Then consider each character's point of view on a topic discussed in the text.

Character 1:

Characters may include: a big boy, Theo, Josh, Izzy,

Character 2:

Ms. Lee, Mr. Park

2. Tell the point of view on a topic for Character 1.

Responses tell the character's point of view.

3. Tell the point of view on a topic for Character 2.

Responses tell the character's point of view.

Children analyze and respond to literary and informational text.

Name _____

DIRECTIONS Revisit pp. 15–18 of *Trouble at the Sandbox*. Draw a picture of the sandbox on a separate piece of paper. Show who is there and what is happening. Then rewrite the scene in a paragraph. Use descriptive details to show what each character did and said.

Responses should include details about what happens and the reactions to what happens.

Conventions

Collective Nouns Circle the collective nouns.

1. community insects herd cows gosling
2. marker army buses committee pod
3. bouquet sweep swarm sequence ants
4. cellphones group brooms team department

Children write routinely for a range of tasks, purposes, and audiences. Children practice various conventions of standard English.

Name _____

Long Vowels Spelled VCe

f<u>a</u>ce m<u>i</u>ce r<u>a</u>ke b<u>o</u>ne

Say the word for each picture.
Write a, e, i, o, or **u** to finish each word.

1. 2. 3. 4.

c a ge r o se r i ce sp a ce

5. 6. 7. 8.

sn a ke sl i ce h o se t a pe

Find the word that has the same middle sound as the picture.
Mark the space to show your answer.

9. love
 swarm
 dive

10. mule
beam
stripe

Children apply grade-level phonics and word analysis skills.

Name _____

DIRECTIONS Write sentences using the words below.

probably mumbled properly nodded

Responses should show contextual understanding of the words.

Write in Response to Reading

DIRECTIONS Reread p. 20 of *Trouble at the Sandbox*. How does the picture on this page help you understand what's happening in the story?

Responses should use text evidence that the boys smile; they aren't afraid of the big boy.

Children demonstrate contextual understanding of Benchmark Vocabulary. Children read text closely and use text evidence in their written answers.

Name _____

DIRECTIONS Look at the description and picture you created for your new character in Lesson 3. Think about the scene when Theo meets this new character. Write a short paragraph or scene that would be the beginning of a chapter about Theo and the new character. Use information you have learned about writing a strong beginning.

Paragraphs should have a strong beginning and be about the character meeting Theo for the first time.

Conventions

Verbs in the Present and Past Tense Circle the present-tense verbs. Underline the past-tense verbs.

1. (swim) (eats) jumped walked (smiles)

2. (run) hopped (jump) jogged volunteered

3. (wish) smiled snowed (rains) trained

4. ran published (turns) (writes) sprinted

 Children write routinely for a range of tasks, purposes, and audiences. Children practice various conventions of standard English.

Name _____

Benchmark Vocabulary

DIRECTIONS Write a sentence using the word below.

corner

<u>Responses should show contextual understanding of</u>

<u>the word.</u>

Write in
Response to
Reading

DIRECTIONS Reread p. 24 of *Trouble at the Sandbox*. Why does Theo hand Ben a truck? What happened in the story that changed the relationship between Theo and Ben? Use examples from the text to support your answer.

<u>Responses will vary but should indicate that Ben</u>

<u>offers to help, and the boys are now friends.</u>

Children demonstrate contextual understanding of Benchmark Vocabulary. Children read text closely and use text evidence in their written answers.

Name _____

DIRECTIONS Using evidence from the text, answer the following questions about pp. 22–24 of *Trouble at the Sandbox.*

1. Reread the last paragraph on p. 22. Why does Theo's heart sink?

<u>He thinks Ben will take the trucks.</u>

2. How has Ben's point of view changed since Chapter 1?

<u>Ben now smiles, thinks building a volcano looks</u>

<u>like fun, and wants to help.</u>

3. List two events from the text that show how Theo's point of view about Ben has changed.

<u>Responses should list events that show Theo</u>

<u>likes Ben.</u>

Children analyze and respond to literary and informational text.

DIRECTIONS Recall the events in *Trouble at the Sandbox,* beginning with the discovery that Ben and his friends have been taking the trucks to make a movie. List three or four major events in chronological order. Then write a paragraph recounting the events in the second half of the text. Use both types of sequence words when writing your paragraph.

Paragraphs include sequence words that list major events. Example: Ms. Lee tells that the boys took the trucks; Ben apologizes; Theo and friends help make the movie; Ben helps build a volcano.

Conventions

Use Simple Sentences Circle the subject in each sentence.

1. Izzy ran into the sandbox.

2. The volcano was bigger than before!

3. The teacher will help the students.

4. Theo ran toward the sandbox!

 Children write routinely for a range of tasks, purposes, and audiences.
Children practice various conventions of standard English.

Name _____

DIRECTIONS Write a sentence using the words below.

tumbling vanished ambling

Responses should show contextual understanding of

the words.

Write in
Response to
Reading

DIRECTIONS Reread pp. 5–7 of *Snowshoe Hare's Winter Home*. Pick one animal that Snowshoe Hare talked with. Write a sentence that tells what Snowshoe Hare thinks about that animal's plan for surviving winter. Use the text to support your answer.

Responses should indicate that he didn't want to

sleep all winter; he didn't want to eat branches.

Children demonstrate contextual
understanding of Benchmark Vocabulary.
Children read text closely and use text
evidence in their written answers.

Name _____

DIRECTIONS Expand on the story you started in Lesson 6 using characters from *Trouble at the Sandbox* and your new character from Lesson 3. Then review the story and decide on one additional event to add to your story. Use details to describe actions, thoughts, and feelings.

Responses should add one additional event to the story, describing the character's thoughts, words, and actions.

Conventions

Identify Irregular Verbs Circle the irregular verbs.

1. At last Snowshoe Hare (saw) the creature in the doorway.
2. The animals (ran) out to the road.
3. The creature (built) his winter shelter.
4. We (met) at the sandbox to build another volcano.

Children write routinely for a range of tasks, purposes, and audiences. Children practice various conventions of standard English.

Name _____

DIRECTIONS Write sentences using the words below.

nibbling thumped crackled

Responses should show contextual understanding of

the words.

> **Write in Response to Reading**

DIRECTIONS In what ways are the settings of *Trouble at the Sandbox* and *Snowshoe Hare's Winter Home* different? Tell at least two ways that they are not the same. Use the text to support your answer.

Responses should indicate ways the settings differ:

the playground, classroom, and/or school as opposed

to the woods, forest, and/or pond.

 Children demonstrate contextual understanding of Benchmark Vocabulary. Children read text closely and use text evidence in their written answers.

Name _____

DIRECTIONS Revisit pp. 5–10 of *Snowshoe Hare's Winter Home*. Think about the plot, or what happened, in this chapter. Then list the major events in the chapter in order below.

1. Bear says to quit fooling around.

2. Beaver says to store food.

3. Turtle says it is time to hibernate.

4. Turtle heads for the pond.

5. Duck invites Snowshoe Hare.

Children analyze and respond to literary and informational text.

Name _____

DIRECTIONS Recall a sequence of events from *Snowshoe Hare's Winter Home* that you want to retell. Write one paragraph about a sequence of at least three events. Use words that tell *when* to support your answer.

Responses will vary but should include three events

in sequence, such as what happens when Snowshoe

meets Bear, Beaver, and Trout. Paragraphs should

include sequence words that tell *when.*

Conventions

Identify Irregular Verbs Circle the correct past-tense verb.

1. The truck (comed, (came)) to a stop.

2. He ((sprang), springed) from the table.

3. The high winds ((blew), blewed) snow around the playground.

4. The snows melted and the grass ((became), becomed) visible again.

Children write routinely for a range of tasks, purposes, and audiences. Children practice various conventions of standard English.

Benchmark Vocabulary

DIRECTIONS Write sentences using the words below.

speck peering bounded

Responses should show contextual understanding of

the words.

Write in Response to Reading

DIRECTIONS Revisit pp. 11–13 of *Snowshoe Hare's Winter Home*. How do the illustrations help you understand the story? Use examples from the text to support your answer.

Responses will vary but might include that he worries

until the hares point out his white fur, shown in the

art, which helps him hide in the snow.

Children demonstrate contextual understanding of Benchmark Vocabulary. Children read text closely and use text evidence in their written answers.

Name _____

DIRECTIONS Using evidence from the text, answer the following questions about pp. 11–13 of *Snowshoe Hare's Winter Home*.

I. Revisit the second paragraph on p. 11. What word best supports the illustration?

Responses will vary but could include freeze *or*

moving.

2. Revisit the third paragraph on p. 11. Where have Snowshoe Hare's friends gone?

Responses should tell where they have gone.

3. Revisit p. 12. Is Snowshoe Hare still alone? Who does he see?

No. He hears friendly voices and sees hares.

Children analyze and respond to literary and informational text.

DIRECTIONS Write a draft of the story you began planning in previous lessons.

Responses will vary but drafts should follow the planning outlined in earlier lessons.

Conventions

Irregular Verbs Write the correct past-tense form of each verb below.

1. weaves wove 3. hangs hung

2. leaps leapt 4. fall fell

Children write routinely for a range of tasks, purposes, and audiences. Children practice various conventions of standard English.

Name _____

Long Vowels Spelled VCe

smil**e** dim**e** pil**e** tim**e**

Say the word for each picture.
Write a, e, i, o, or **u** to finish each word.

1.

m **u** le

2.

sl **i** ce

3.

m **i** ce

4.

sp **a** ce

5.

c **a** pe

6.

gr **a** pe

Find the word that has the same middle sound as the picture.
Mark the space to show your answer.

7. hose

cart
 mule

8. mug
clip
 bite

 Children apply grade-level phonics and word
analysis skills.

Unit 1 • Module A • Lesson 11 • 31

Name _____

DIRECTIONS Write sentences using the words below.

frost orchards amber

Responses should show contextual understanding of the words.

DIRECTIONS Revisit the poem "Something Told the Wild Geese." What are two facts you learn about geese by reading the poem? Use evidence from the poem to support your answer.

Responses should include two facts such as wild geese leave when it snows, and they have warm feathers.

 Children demonstrate contextual understanding of Benchmark Vocabulary. Children read text closely and use text evidence in their written answers.

Name _____

DIRECTIONS Revise the draft of the story you have been working on. Review your introduction, paragraphs, sentences, and conclusion. Make notes about where changes are needed as you review.

Children should review their drafts, noting how to edit

the introduction, body, and conclusion.

Conventions

Pronouns Circle the pronouns in the sentences below. Then write a sentence of your own using a pronoun.

1. (He) was cold.

2. (She) liked the snow.

3. (They) read a poem about geese.

4. **The sentence should include one pronoun.**

Children write routinely for a range of tasks, purposes, and audiences. Children practice various conventions of standard English.

Name _____

DIRECTIONS Write sentences using the words below.

sharing scared vanished

Responses should show contextual understanding of

the words.

DIRECTIONS Think about the characters in *Trouble at the Sandbox* and *Snowshoe Hare's Winter Home.* Which character's point of view do you most agree with? Use examples from the text to support your answer.

Responses should describe a character's point of

view and offer reasons why the child agrees with it.

Children demonstrate contextual understanding of Benchmark Vocabulary. Children read text closely and use text evidence in their written answers.

Lesson 12

Name _____

Reading Analysis

DIRECTIONS Using evidence from *Trouble at the Sandbox* and *Snowshoe Hare's Winter Home,* follow the directions below.

1. Name two characters from *Trouble at the Sandbox* or *Snowshoe Hare's Winter Home* that have different points of view.

Character 1: <u>Responses name two characters</u>

Character 2: <u>who have different viewpoints.</u>

2. Tell the point of view on a topic for Character 1.

<u>Responses tell the character's point of view on</u>

<u>a topic.</u>

3. Tell the point of view on a topic for Character 2.

<u>Responses tell the character's point of view on</u>

<u>the same topic.</u>

Children analyze and respond to literary and informational text.

Unit 1 • Module A • Lesson 12 • 35

Name _____

DIRECTIONS Edit the draft of the new story you have worked on in previous lessons. Check capitalization, punctuation, spelling, and grammar. Review the title, author name, and paragraph indentation. Use a colored pen or pencil to mark changes.

Children check capitalization, punctuation, spelling,

grammar, and indentation. They review the title and

author.

Conventions

Pronouns Write the correct pronoun in the blank.

1. He leaped back as water splashed <u>him</u>.

2. Snowshoe Hare will spend the winter with <u>them</u>.

3. Ms. Lee is a nice teacher. <u>Her</u> voice is always relaxed.

4. The big boys were mean to Theo. Then <u>they</u> walked away.

Children write routinely for a range of tasks, purposes, and audiences. Children practice various conventions of standard English.

Name _____

DIRECTIONS Write sentences using the words below.

probably snuggle

Responses should show contextual understanding of

the words.

DIRECTIONS What happens at the end of *Trouble at the Sandbox*? How do things change for Theo, Izzy, and Josh? Use examples from the text to support your answer.

Responses should use evidence from the text

indicating that the boys are friends with Ben and are

not afraid of him.

Children demonstrate contextual understanding of
Benchmark Vocabulary. Children read text closely
and use text evidence in their written answers.

Name _____

A Birthday Surprise

"Mom will be so surprised!" Sadie said. She looked proudly at the cake that Uncle Curt had helped her and her brother Sam make for Mom's birthday.

"Let's put it in the dining room," Sam said. "That way it will be the first thing Mom sees."

Sadie agreed, and Sam carefully picked it up. Then trouble arrived. Their cousin Wes bounded through the swinging door. The door bumped the plate, the plate tipped, and splat! The cake landed on the floor.

"Oh, no!" Sadie cried. "What can we do now?"

"We'll have to be creative," Sam said.

Uncle Curt had made them pancakes that morning before he left for work, and they still had leftovers. "We can't give Mom a birthday cake. Let's give her birthday pancakes instead!" Sadie said.

"Great idea!" said Sam. They warmed the pancakes. Sam spread jam on each one. Then Sadie put on banana slices. They stacked the pancakes and put candles on the top.

Children read text closely to determine what the text says.

Name _____

Just then, they heard Mom coming down the stairs. Sam raced to the stairs and asked her to stay in her bedroom. Mom thought there might be a surprise. Then Sadie arrived with the birthday pancakes. Mom laughed. "How did you know that I have always wanted to have a birthday breakfast in bed?" she said.

Look for Clues
Underline the text that tells about Sadie's talents and personality.

Ask Questions
Write a question that you might ask someone who has had to fix a problem quickly. **Responses will vary.**

Example: What did you do?

Make Your Case
Underline the first major event. Then underline the next major event.

Make Your Case: Extend Your Ideas
Explain why sequence is important in a story. Use examples from this story. **Responses will vary.**

Example: Sequence helps readers follow and

understand the story.

 Children read text closely to determine what the text says.

Type your story on a computer and print it out. Follow these steps:

- Open and save your document.
- Add the story title and your name at the top of the page.
- Make your editing corrections as you type.
- Read your document to make sure you made all the corrections and that you did not make any typing mistakes.
- Print your document and read it one last time.

Responses will vary, but children should add a title and their name, make corrections, and print the document.

Conventions

Reflexive Pronouns Circle the reflexive pronoun in each sentence.

1. I like (myself.)

2. "Take a look at (yourself!)" they said.

3. We can make the volcano (ourselves.)

4. I wish the big boys would play among (themselves.)

Children write routinely for a range of tasks, purposes, and audiences. Children practice various conventions of standard English.

Name _____

Consonant Blends

Say the word for each picture.
Pick the letters from the box that finish each word.

| bl | sl | nt | cl | nd | sk | st | str | fr | spl |

1.

2.

3.

4.

blimp **ca**st **ma**sk **cl**ip

Read each sentence. **Add** the missing letters to the word or words. **Use** the box above for help.

5. My **fr**____iend Sam and I put up a te **nt**____.

6. Our **sl**____eeping bags were on the grou **nd**____.

7. They seemed to be on a **sl**____ ant.

8. We **str**____ etched out on our backs.

9. I **spl**____ashed water on my face to **st**____ay awake.

Children apply grade-level phonics and word analysis skills.

Name _____

DIRECTIONS Write sentences using the words below.

exchange facts subway country

Responses should show contextual understanding of the words.

Write in Response to Reading

DIRECTIONS Revisit pp. 6–7 of *Friends Around the World*. Who is telling the story? Why are they telling the story? Use examples from the text to support your answer.

Responses will vary but should include that Isabel and Hau tell the story. They are e-pals.

Children demonstrate contextual understanding of Benchmark Vocabulary. Children read text closely and use text evidence in their written answers.

Name _____

DIRECTIONS Draw a picture of a rural area. Then write a caption for your picture.

The picture should show a rural area, and the caption should tell about the picture.

Conventions

Identify Adjectives Adjectives describe nouns. Circle the adjectives in the sentences below.

1. The (loud) subway was Isabel's (favorite) part about going to school.

2. The elevator in her building was (cold) and (unpleasant.)

3. The (big) apartment building towered over the park.

4. Her motorcycle bounced up and down on the (bumpy) roads of Ho Chi Minh City.

Children write routinely for a range of tasks, purposes, and audiences.
Children practice various conventions of standard English.

Name _____

DIRECTIONS Write sentences using the words below.

uniform parka outback

Responses should show contextual understanding of

the words.

DIRECTIONS Revisit pp. 12–13 of *Friends Around the World*. What details does Dan provide that help you understand where he lives? Use examples from the text to support your answer.

Responses should use evidence from the text to

indicate that Dan lives on a farm; the farm is far from

any town; animals are on the farm.

Children demonstrate contextual understanding of Benchmark Vocabulary. Children read text closely and use text evidence in their written answers.

Name _____

DIRECTIONS Look at the photos and captions on pp. 8–13 of *Friends Around the World*. Think about a photo you would like to add to one of these pages. Write a description of that photo and the caption that you would include with it. Which key details would this photo support?

Responses will vary.

Children describe one photo, write a caption, and tell which key details in the text are supported by the photo.

Children analyze and respond to literary and informational text.

DIRECTIONS Select one of the places mentioned in *Friends Around the World* and describe it using facts provided by the writer. Be sure to use adjectives in your description.

<u>Responses use text evidence and adjectives</u>

<u>to describe New York City, Ho Chi Minh City, or</u>

<u>Yellowknife.</u>

Conventions

Identifying Adjectives Complete the sentence by adding an adjective.

1. It was a <u>Responses will vary but may</u>

<u>include *rainy*</u> _____ day, so Isabel stayed inside.

2. When I woke up it was <u>Responses will vary but may</u>

<u>include *cold*</u> _____,

so my Mom made me put on a hat.

 Children write routinely for a range of tasks, purposes, and audiences.
Children practice various conventions of standard English.

Name _____

DIRECTIONS Write sentences using the words below.

favorite scored traditional

Responses should show contextual understanding of the words.

Write in
Response to
Reading

DIRECTIONS Revisit pp. 16–17 of *Friends Around the World*. What are Hau's favorite things to eat? Use examples from the text to support your answer.

Hau says she thinks noodle soup is yummy. She loves fruit, especially dragon fruit.

 Children demonstrate contextual
understanding of Benchmark Vocabulary.
Children read text closely and use text
evidence in their written answers.

Name _____

DIRECTIONS Using the text, answer the following questions about pp. 14–17 of *Friends Around the World*.

1. What is the main idea on pp. 14–15?

The main idea is Isabel likes sports.

2. List two details that support the main idea.

Responses should list details such as she plays

soccer and baseball.

3. What is the main idea on pp. 16–17?

Hau tells what are her favorite foods.

4. List two details that support the main idea.

Responses should list details such as Hau thinks

noodle soup is yummy; she loves fruit.

Children analyze and respond to literary and informational text.

Name _____

DIRECTIONS Look over the list the class made about pp. 14–17 of *Friends Around the World*. Choose one of these topics and write a list of questions about the topic that you want answered.

Responses will vary but questions should relate to a topic from the class-generated list.

Conventions

Adjectives Read the paragraph. Circle the adjectives.

One sunny day, I went to a baseball game. Soon the yellow sun peeked out from behind the clouds. My favorite team wore white uniforms with black stripes. Before long, I had two delicious hot dogs to eat!

Children write routinely for a range of tasks, purposes, and audiences.
Children practice various conventions of standard English.

Name _____

DIRECTIONS Write sentences using the words below.

frozen meal caribou

Responses should show contextual understanding of the words.

DIRECTIONS Revisit pp. 18–19 of *Friends Around the World*. What does Akiak's father do that he wants to do when he gets older? Use examples from the text to support your answer.

Akiak's father competes in a race. Akiak says, "Maybe one day I will too."

Children demonstrate contextual understanding of Benchmark Vocabulary. Children read text closely and use text evidence in their written answers.

Name _____

DIRECTIONS Write a paragraph in which you identify the author's purpose in *Friends Around the World*. Use details from the text to support your answer.

The author's purpose is to inform readers about

different cultures. Responses should use details from

the text.

Identifying Adjectives Write your own sentences using adjectives from *Friends Around the World*.

1. Responses will vary, but each sentence should

2. include an adjective. Example: Akiak's favorite

3. meal was caribou!

Children write routinely for a range of tasks, purposes, and audiences. Children practice various conventions of standard English.

Unit 1 • Module B • Lesson 4 • 51

Name _____

DIRECTIONS Write sentences using the words below.

seasons pours floods

Responses should show contextual understanding of

the words.

DIRECTIONS Revisit pp. 24–25 of *Friends Around the World*. How does the picture on this page support the words? Use details from the text to support your answer.

During the dry season, Hau plays in a park, one of

which is shown. During the rainy season, the streets

flood, which the photo shows.

Children demonstrate contextual understanding of Benchmark Vocabulary. Children read text closely and use text evidence in their written answers.

Name _____

DIRECTIONS Look at the photos and captions on pp. 22–25 of *Friends Around the World*. For each page, write the page number and then a sentence that tells what you learned from the photo and caption on that page.

Page 22: there are interesting things at the museum; page 23: Isabel loves Central Park in the winter; page 24: there are great playgrounds in Ho Chi Minh City; page 25: streets flood but people still go out.

Children analyze and respond to literary and informational text.

Name _____

DIRECTIONS Revisit pp. 24–25 of *Friends Around the World*. Then write a paragraph using facts about Ho Chi Minh City. Use evidence from the text to support your answer.

Responses will vary but might include: rivers flood

the streets, but people still go outside; kids love

playing on the great playgrounds.

Conventions

Review Adjectives Replace each bold print adjective with a new adjective.

1. I wore my **wooly** sweater today.

Example: *itchy*

2. We had **sweet** fruit for dessert.

Example: *fresh*

3. It's always very **warm** in Ho Chi Minh City.

Example: *humid*

Children write routinely for a range of tasks, purposes, and audiences. Children practice various conventions of standard English.

Name _____

Endings -s, -ed, -ing

talk talk**s** lift lift**ing** drop drop**ped** smile smil**ing**

Use the word in () to finish each sentence.
Add *-s, -ed,* **or** *-ing* to make a word.
Write the new word on the line.

1. Isabel ____hugs____ Dad. (hug)

2. Mom ____waves____ good-bye. (wave)

3. Isabel ____grabbed____ her hat and went to school. (grab)

4. This is an ____exciting____ day. (excite)

5. Akiak and his dad are going ____fishing____. (fish)

Children apply grade-level phonics and word analysis skills.

Name _____

DIRECTIONS Write sentences using the words below.

bandage barbecue

Responses should show contextual understanding of

the words.

DIRECTIONS Revisit pp. 28–29 of *Friends Around the World*. What is the purpose of the Royal Flying Doctor Service? Why couldn't Dan's mom drive him to the hospital? Use examples from the text to support your answer.

Responses should use text evidence including the

service helps people get to hospitals. Mom couldn't

drive because the hospital is too far away.

Children demonstrate contextual understanding of Benchmark Vocabulary. Children read text closely and use text evidence in their written answers.

Name _____

DIRECTIONS Choose one of the children that you have read about in *Friends Around the World*. Write about what that child does using key words to help you describe them. Use details from the text to help you write your response.

Responses should include a description of what one

child does, using text details. Example: Dan lives

in the Australian outback. He goes to the School of

the Air. His teacher gives him homework over the

internet.

Conventions

Adverbs Circle the adverb in each sentence.

I. Dan (softly) caressed his chicken.

2. (Tomorrow) Grandpa will come for a visit.

3. It snowed (heavily), so they closed the school.

4. Dan hurt his leg, but he will be better (soon).

Children write routinely for a range of tasks, purposes, and audiences. Children practice various conventions of standard English.

Name _____

Benchmark Vocabulary

DIRECTIONS Write sentences using the words below.

learned common activities exciting

Responses should show contextual understanding of
the words.

Write in
Response to
Reading

DIRECTIONS Revisit p. 30 of *Friends Around the World*.
What does Isabel say she has in common with her new
friends? Use details from the text to support your answer.

Responses should indicate that Isabel and her
friends have schoolwork, that they like to have fun,
and that there are exciting things to do in all the
places.

Children demonstrate contextual understanding of
Benchmark Vocabulary. Children read text closely and
use text evidence in their written answers.

Name _____

DIRECTIONS Revisit pp. 30–32 of *Friends Around the World*. How does the glossary help you understand the text? Use examples from the text to support your answer.

Responses will vary but should use evidence from the text to explain that the glossary helps readers know the meaning of unfamiliar words. If, for example, the reader doesn't know the definition of *caribou*, the reader could find the definition in the glossary.

Children analyze and respond to literary and informational text.

Name _____

DIRECTIONS Think about the two cities that you read about in *Friends Around the World*—New York City and Ho Chi Minh City. Write a few sentences that tell how these cities are alike and different. Use linking words to connect your ideas about each city.

Responses include linking words to show how the

cities are alike and different. Example: Both are cities,

but one is in the U.S., and the other is in Vietnam.

Conventions

Adverbs Add an adverb to each sentence.

1. The girls will go swimming **Answers will vary but may**

 include *tomorrow* .

2. Akiak **Answers will vary but may include** *quietly*

 _____ closed the door behind her.

Children write routinely for a range of tasks, purposes, and audiences. Children practice various conventions of standard English.

Name _____

DIRECTIONS Write sentences using the words below.

mighty fierce

Responses should show contextual understanding of the words.

Write in Response to Reading

DIRECTIONS Before Chrissy and Jenny lived at 107 Maple Street, other people lived on the land. Tell how these other people lived on the land before there was a house built on it. Use details from the text to support your answer.

Responses should use text evidence to tell that people who followed the buffalo herd lived there in teepees near the stream. They stayed for the summer.

Children demonstrate contextual understanding of Benchmark Vocabulary. Children read text closely and use text evidence in their written answers.

Name _____

Unlikely Friends

Every Monday afternoon, Anya helped Ms. Hickson with her yardwork. Ms. Hickson always watched Anya from her tall porch. She even had a glass of juice waiting for her when the work was done. Anya often brought along her violin. Ms. Hickson would beam with delight when Anya played for her. Anya used to complain about visiting Ms. Hickson, but Anya's mother always insisted she go. She said that neighbors should take care of each other.

One Monday, Anya came without her violin. When she finished raking the yard, she sat down sadly beside her neighbor. Ms. Hickson asked what had happened. Anya burst into tears. Her brother had broken her violin by accident. There was no way it could be fixed in time for her fall concert. Ms. Hickson disappeared into the house. She returned a few minutes later with an old violin case. Inside was the most beautiful violin Anya had ever seen. Ms. Hickson picked it up lovingly and handed it to Anya. Anya played a few notes, laid the violin in its velvet-lined case, and threw her arms around Ms. Hickson. The violin was the best gift Anya had ever received.

Children read text closely to determine what the text says.

Name _____

Look for Clues

Underline the text that tells how Anya and Ms. Hickson were good neighbors.

Look for Clues: Extend Your Ideas

What word tells you how important the violin was to Ms. Hickson? Circle it.

Ask Questions

Write two questions you might ask Ms. Hickson if you were visiting her.

Responses should be based on information in the story. Example: Is the violin yours? Do you still play?

Make Your Case

Underline the text that supports what we know about the relationship between Anya and Ms. Hickson.

Make Your Case: Extend Your Ideas

Circle the text that tells how Anya used to feel about Ms. Hickson.

Children read text closely to determine what the text says.

Name _____

DIRECTIONS On a separate sheet of paper, draw a picture of a rural setting from *The House on Maple Street*. Then write a paragraph that introduces the time period, gives several details about the setting, and concludes by telling why the time period is important.

The time was 300 years ago. The setting had a stream, flowers, and grass, but no house. During this time, people made arrowheads, which is why the time period is important.

Conventions

Adverbs Underline the adverbs in the sentences below. Then write your own sentence using an adverb.

1. The rabbits <u>suddenly</u> jumped out of the bushes.

2. <u>After</u> reading *The House on Maple Street*, I wondered what the area near my house will look like in the future.

3. Sentence should have an adverb.

Children write routinely for a range of tasks, purposes, and audiences. Children practice various conventions of standard English.

Name _____

DIRECTIONS Write sentences using the words below.

snug complained

Responses should show contextual understanding of

the words.

> **Write in Response to Reading**

DIRECTIONS Write your opinion about whether the changes made by the people at 107 Maple Street were good or bad. Use examples from the text to support your thoughts.

Responses will vary but might include an opinion

that the changes were good because people built

roads and houses.

Children demonstrate contextual understanding of Benchmark Vocabulary. Children read text closely and use text evidence in their written answers.

Name _____

DIRECTIONS Revisit pp. 14–16 of *The House on Maple Street*. How does the author use language to show that the location is the same, but the time is different? How do the visuals in the story help you understand what is taking place and when?

The author's first sentence on page 16 indicates a different time and uses the word *here*. A visual shows maple trees, and on page 15, the same address is given.

Children analyze and respond to literary and informational text.

Name _____

DIRECTIONS Research the area around your home and how it has changed over time. Interview your parents or neighbors and ask about how the area around your home has changed over time. Then draw a picture on a separate sheet of paper showing how it looks now and write sentences describing the neighborhood as it looks today.

Children draw pictures showing how their neighborhood looks today.

Conventions

Use Adverbs Circle the adverbs that tell *when* and *where*. Then write two sentences of your own that use one of the adverbs below.

1. Circle the adverbs that tell *when*.

 (yesterday) slowly sweetly (daily) (later)

2. Circle the adverbs that tell *where*.

 loudly (behind) (around) snowed soon

3. **Responses will vary, but each sentence should**

4. **have a circled adverb.**

Children write routinely for a range of tasks, purposes, and audiences. Children practice various conventions of standard English.

Unit 1 • Module B • Lesson 9 • 67

Name _____

DIRECTIONS Write sentences using the words below.

paved remained

Responses should show contextual understanding of

the words.

Write in Response to Reading

DIRECTIONS Tell your opinion about whether you would want to live on Maple Street. Use details from the text to support your opinion.

Responses will vary but should use text evidence to

support the opinion. Example: I want to live there. I

love the trees.

Children demonstrate contextual understanding of Benchmark Vocabulary. Children read text closely and use text evidence in their written answers.

Name _____

DIRECTIONS The story structure of *The House on Maple Street* begins in the present time. It then jumps back to 300 years ago. Readers then follow the story of this place until they read once again about present times.

Beginning with the events 300 years ago, make a list of 5 events that take place in chronological order. Include the page numbers where these events are found. **Examples are given.**

1. Animals drink at the spring. (p. 16)

2. A storm roars across the forest. (p. 17)

3. Next spring, flowers grow. (p. 18)

4. Buffalo come. (p. 19)

5. People follow the buffalo. (p. 20)

Children analyze and respond to literary and informational text.

Name _____

Writing

DIRECTIONS Using the information you learned from interviewing your parents or neighbors, draw a second picture of how your neighborhood looked in the past. Write sentences using descriptive details to explain your drawing. Then compare how your neighborhood is now to how it was in the past. The drawing should reflect how the child's neighborhood looked in the past.

The sentences compare then to now.

Conventions

Use Adverbs Complete the sentences below using adverbs.

1. The child Responses will vary but may include

 slowly. walked to school.

2. My sister Responses will vary but may include

 carefully. painted my fingernails.

Children write routinely for a range of tasks, purposes, and audiences.
Children practice various conventions of standard English.

Name _____

Endings -s, -ed, -ing

scream scream**s** cry cry**ing** slip slipp**ed** run runn**ing**

Use the word in () to finish each sentence.
Add -s, -ed, or -ing to make a word.
Write the new word on the line.

1. Isabel _____skipped_____ to the subway
 because she was excited. (skip)

2. I hope we are there when she _____wins_____ the
 prize. (win)

3. The little boy was _____yelling_____ because he injured
 his knee. (yell)

4. The frog _____hopped_____ out of the fox's way! (hop)

5. Hau sometimes liked to go _____swimming_____ after
 school. (swim)

Children apply grade-level phonics and word
analysis skills.

Name _____

DIRECTIONS Write sentences using the words below.

cricket mighty

Responses should show contextual understanding of

the words.

DIRECTIONS Revisit pp. 20–21 of *Friends Around the World* and pp. 34–35 of *The House on Maple Street*. Compare the illustrations in the two texts. Tell one way they are alike and one way they are different.

The illustrations reenforce the content but one uses

photos, and the other uses art. Pages 20–21 show

modern-day times, and pp. 34–35 show a past time.

Children demonstrate contextual understanding of Benchmark Vocabulary. Children read text closely and use text evidence in their written answers.

Name _____

DIRECTIONS Refer to your drawings and your graphic organizers. Write a paragraph in which you compare and contrast the two homes. You should introduce your topic in the first sentence and conclude the paragraph in the last sentence.

Responses will vary but should compare and

contrast the two homes. The first sentence

introduces the topic, and the last sentence is the

conclusion.

Conventions

Contractions Rewrite the sentences below using contractions.

1. Juanita did not do her homework.

Juanita didn't do her homework.

2. Scott has not played baseball in a long time.

Scott hasn't played baseball in a long time.

Children write routinely for a range of tasks, purposes, and audiences.
Children practice various conventions of standard English.

Name _____

DIRECTIONS Write a sentence using the word below.

outback

Responses should show contextual understanding of the word.

Write in Response to Reading

DIRECTIONS Revisit pp. 32–33 of *The House on Maple Street* and pp. 12–13 of *Friends Around the World*. How is Dan's farm different from the farm in *The House on Maple Street*? Use examples from both texts to support your answer.

Responses might include that the farm has animals, but the land looks dry. The other farm also has animals but is green and has a stream.

Children demonstrate contextual understanding of Benchmark Vocabulary. Children read text closely and use text evidence in their written answers.

Name _____

DIRECTIONS Using examples from *The House on Maple Street* and *Friends Around the World*, choose two words and phrases from each text that help you understand what is happening. Then use each of those words and phrases in your own sentences. **Responses will vary.**

1. The House on Maple Street:

Example: A few sturdy flowers lived through the drought.

2.

Example: I hid money in the stump of a burned tree.

3. Friends Around the World:

Example: My dad uses the Internet to shop.

4.

Example: My sister always competes in the marathon.

Children analyze and respond to literary and informational text.

Name _____

DIRECTIONS Revise the explanatory piece that you worked on in Lessons 10 and 11 using peer feedback. Edit your piece for spelling and capitalization. Then make a clean final copy to share. Use *Friends Around the World* and *The House on Maple Street* to look for ideas and examples.

Children edit their writing for errors and then write a final copy.

Conventions

Contractions Rewrite the underlined words as contractions. Don't forget to use apostrophes. Then write a sentence of your own that uses a contraction.

1. <u>She is</u> reading us a good book. She's _____

2. <u>They have</u> been painting the house. They've _____

3. <u>We would</u> like to go to the zoo. We'd _____

4. _____
The sentence should have a contraction.

Children write routinely for a range of tasks, purposes, and audiences.
Children practice various conventions of standard English.

Name _____

Consonant Digraphs *ch, tch, sh, th, wh*

chicken wa**tch** **sh**ip **th**irty **wh**eel

Say the word for each picture.
Write ch, tch, sh, th, or **wh** to finish each word.

1. 2. 3. 4.

whale i**tch** ma**th** **ch**erry

5. 6. 7. 8.

sheep fi**sh** ha**tch** ba**th**

Write a sentence using each word.

9. that *Responses include the word that.*

10. thrill *Responses include the word thrill.*

 Children apply grade-level phonics and word analysis skills.

Name _____

Benchmark Vocabulary

DIRECTIONS Write a sentence using the word below.

save

<u>Responses should show contextual understanding of</u>

<u>the word.</u>

Write in Response to Reading

DIRECTIONS Write several sentences about Alexander. What does he do, think, and feel? Use details from the text to support your answer.

<u>Responses will vary but might include that Alexander</u>

<u>thinks it is unfair that he has no money. He looks</u>

<u>upset.</u>

Children demonstrate contextual understanding of Benchmark Vocabulary. Children read text closely and use text evidence in their written answers.

DIRECTIONS Write several sentences about the decisions Alexander made about spending his money. How does he react to his decisions? Revisit the text and illustrations to find examples of the decisions Alexander made.

Responses may include that he made poor decisions;

he got a dopey deck of cards, a one-eyed bear, and a

melted candle.

Conventions

Singular Possessives Circle the singular possessives. Then write your own sentences using singular possessives.

1. dogs' (sister's) (friend's) girls' (Mom's)

2. Both sentences should include singular

3. possessives.

Children write routinely for a range of tasks, purposes, and audiences. Children practice various conventions of standard English.

Lesson 2

Name _____

Benchmark Vocabulary

DIRECTIONS Write sentences using the words below.

college downtown

Responses should show contextual understanding of the words.

Write in
Response to
Reading

DIRECTIONS Revisit the illustrations on pp. 1–15 of *Alexander, Who Used to Be Rich Last Sunday*. Do the illustrations help you to better understand Alexander as a character? Use examples from the text to support your opinion.

His facial expressions show how he feels. He has a sense of humor because he laughs about planting the dollar.

Children demonstrate contextual understanding of Benchmark Vocabulary. Children read text closely and use text evidence in their written answers.

Name _____

DIRECTIONS Look at the illustration on p. 11 of *Alexander, Who Used to Be Rich Last Sunday.* Using evidence from the text, write several sentences that explain what the illustration tells you about the characters Alexander, Anthony, and Nick.

Responses will vary but might include that the boys really like money. Alexander is holding the dollar up to his face to hide how much he loves money.

Children analyze and respond to literary and informational text.

DIRECTIONS Tell about how the illustrations in *Alexander, Who Used to Be Rich Last Sunday* help you understand what sort of character Alexander is. Use examples from the text to support your answer.

Responses will vary but might indicate that

Alexander loves money and that he looks upset when

he loses his money.

Conventions

Plural Possessives Circle the plural possessives. Then write two of your own sentences using plural possessives.

I. (kittens') student's (cousins') (boys') dad's

2. Responses should include a plural possessive.

3. Responses should include a plural possessive.

Children write routinely for a range of tasks, purposes, and audiences. Children practice various conventions of standard English.

DIRECTIONS Write sentences using the words below.

fined accident

Responses should show contextual understanding of

the words.

Write in
Response to
Reading

DIRECTIONS Review the web you completed. Write about one way Alexander responded to losing or spending his money. Use examples from the text to support your answer.

Responses might include that he was unhappy when

his mom made him pay and when his dad fined him.

Children demonstrate contextual understanding of
Benchmark Vocabulary. Children read text closely
and use text evidence in their written answers.

Name _____

I'll Trade You!

Samuel couldn't wait to show his mom and grandma the new skateboard he had just gotten from Ben. Ben couldn't wait to give his sister the new shawl he had just gotten from Samuel. Ben and Samuel were best friends!

Samuel's grandma had worked for weeks knitting the shawl. Ben had wondered for weeks what to get his sister for her birthday. Then one night Ben saw the shawl Samuel's grandma was knitting. He knew his sister would love it!

Samuel spent every day after school skateboarding with Ben. Samuel wished for his own skateboard. Ben knew how much Samuel would love having a skateboard. Suddenly a trade was born!

Trading one thing for another was a way of life. Samuel's mom and grandma remembered when people used something called money instead. Money paid for things they needed. Samuel and Ben were too young to remember that time.

Sometimes, Samuel's mother opened a secret drawer in her jewelry box. She let him hold the shiny coins and smooth dollar bills she had saved. Then they were put away for safekeeping.

Children read text closely to determine what the text says.

People no longer used money. They traded things instead. Samuel couldn't imagine life any other way. Samuel knew how to draw, so he always traded his drawings to get what he wanted. His family and Ben's family traded often. Samuel didn't understand why anyone might need money. Trading was so much easier!

Look for Clues

Underline details that support the fact that this story takes place in the future.

Ask Questions

On a separate sheet of paper, write a question you would ask Samuel and Ben about life without money.
Example: Do you wish you had money?

Make Your Case

Underline the text that tells the most important idea the writer wants to share with readers about trading.

Make Your Case: Extend Your Ideas

Do you agree that trading is easier than using money? Write an opinion about this.

Responses will vary but should include reasons for the opinion.

Children read text closely to determine what the text says.

Name _____

DIRECTIONS Revisit p. 17 of *Alexander, Who Used to Be Rich Last Sunday*. Consider Alexander's actions in this scene. Then write a narrative sentence for each event on the page. Use specific words to describe the actions seen in the illustrations.

Responses may include that he tries to hold his

breath, but can't. He tries to land on his feet when

he jumps, but the art shows he is about to land on

his back.

Conventions

Apostrophes Underline the contractions. Circle the possessive nouns.

1. can't don't isn't (kids')

2. I've used the last bus pass!

3. I can't find the (child's) hat.

Children write routinely for a range of tasks, purposes, and audiences. Children practice various conventions of standard English.

DIRECTIONS Write sentences using the words below.

coins bargain savings

Responses should show contextual understanding of the words.

Write in Response to Reading

DIRECTIONS Think about how the characters in the story solved their problem. Then write a few sentences that tell how the girl earns money to help her family. Use examples from the text to support your answer.

Responses will vary but should indicate that the girl gets paid for working in the diner.

Children demonstrate contextual understanding of Benchmark Vocabulary. Children read text closely and use text evidence in their written answers.

Name _____

DIRECTIONS Using evidence from the text, write sentences about the beginning, middle, and end of *A Chair for My Mother*. Use details from the text to support your answer.

Beginning:

Responses will vary but may include that a fire

destroys the furniture.

Middle:

Responses will vary but may include that the family

saves coins.

End:

Responses will vary but may include that the

family buys the chair.

Children analyze and respond to literary and informational text.

Name _____

DIRECTIONS On a separate sheet of paper, write a new beginning to *A Chair for My Mother*. Start your new beginning at the time of the fire. Include vivid details to describe the fire. Revisit *A Chair for My Mother* to find details that show how the girl and her mother discovered the fire.

Children should write a new beginning to the story that includes vivid details.

Conventions

Possessive Pronouns Write your own sentences using possessive pronouns.

1. Responses will vary but should include a possessive pronoun.

2. Responses will vary but should include a possessive pronoun.

3. Responses will vary but should include a possessive pronoun.

 Children write routinely for a range of tasks, purposes, and audiences. Children practice various conventions of standard English.

Name _____

DIRECTIONS Write sentences using the words below.

spoiled charcoal

Responses should show contextual understanding of the words.

Write in
Response to
Reading

DIRECTIONS Revisit pp. 50–67 of *A Chair for My Mother*. Write several sentences about your opinion of the girl's character. Use details from the text to support your answer.

Responses might include the girl is caring; she saves some money to buy the chair.

Children demonstrate contextual understanding of Benchmark Vocabulary. Children read text closely and use text evidence in their written answers.

Name _____

DIRECTIONS Using evidence from the text, answer the following questions about pp. 50–67 of *A Chair for My Mother*.

1. Reread p. 53. What does this page tell you about the girl's character?

She is a good worker, and she is caring because she

puts money into the jar.

2. Reread the last paragraph on p. 55. Write several sentences about whether or not you think the girl's mother works hard. Use details from the text to support your answer.

Responses should indicate that her mother works

hard. Often, she is so tired from working that she

falls asleep while the girl counts the change.

Children analyze and respond to literary and informational text.

DIRECTIONS Revisit the first half of *A Chair for My Mother*. Choose an event and write dialogue between the narrator and her mother about that event. Remember to use details to describe the characters' thoughts or feelings.

Responses might include when Mama laughs when

she comes home: "Mama, you're happy tonight. What

happened at work?" "One customer gave me a big tip!"

Conventions

Possessive Pronouns Circle the possessive pronouns in the sentences below. Then write your own sentence using a possessive pronoun.

1. This house is (ours.)

2. Is this (your) ruler?

3. Responses will vary but should include a

possessive pronoun. Example: That is my ruler.

Children write routinely for a range of tasks, purposes, and audiences. Children practice various conventions of standard English.

Lesson 6

Name _____

Phonics

r-Controlled *ar, or, ore, oar*

arm

h**orn**

c**ore**

oar

Pick a word from the box to match each picture.
Write the word on the line.

artist	bark	garden	roar	score
store	stork	storm	start	short

1.

storm

2.

store

3.

roar

4.

stork

5.

bark

6.

artist

7.

score

8.

garden

Pick a word that is the opposite of each word below.
Write the word on the line.

9. stop start

10. tall short

 Children apply grade-level phonics and word analysis skills.

Unit 2 • Module A • Lessons 6 • 93

Name _____

DIRECTIONS Write sentences using the words below.

exchanged boost

Responses should show contextual understanding of the words.

Write in Response to Reading

DIRECTIONS Revisit pp. 75–79 of *A Chair for My Mother*. Write several sentences about why the girl was not allowed to ride in the back of the truck while the chair was being delivered. Use details from the text to support your answer.

Responses might include that it was not safe, but she did sit in it when they took it to the door.

Children demonstrate contextual understanding of Benchmark Vocabulary. Children read text closely and use text evidence in their written answers.

Name _____

DIRECTIONS Write about the next item that the family will save up for. Include one detail that describes the item and one detail that describes the reason the family would want to save for the item. Revisit *A Chair for My Mother* to look for ideas about what the family might purchase.

Responses might suggest, for example, that they

might want to buy a sofa so everyone may have a

place to sit.

Conventions

Simple Sentences Circle the simple sentences below. Then write your own simple sentence.

1. The sun was hot that day, so the pool felt cool.
 (I had fun.)

2. Although I couldn't ride in the truck, I was excited for the chair to be delivered. (I was happy!)

3. Responses should include a simple sentence.

Example: You are lucky!

 Children write routinely for a range of tasks, purposes, and audiences. Children practice various conventions of standard English.

Name _____

DIRECTIONS Write a sentence using the word below.

rich

Response should show contextual understanding of

the word.

> **Write in**
> **Response to**
> **Reading**

DIRECTIONS Write your thoughts about how the author structured the story—telling readers how it ends on the first page. Use details from the text to support your answer.

Responses will vary but should indicate a supported

opinion about the story's structure.

Children demonstrate contextual understanding of Benchmark Vocabulary. Children read text closely and use text evidence in their written answers.

Name _____

DIRECTIONS Review the story sequence chart for *Alexander, Who Used to Be Rich Last Sunday*. Draw three pictures: one showing something that happened first, a second showing something that happened in the middle of the story, and a third picture showing something that happened last.

Responses will vary but drawings should show the correct sequence of events as they are listed on the story sequence chart.

DIRECTIONS Write a new ending to *Alexander, Who Used to Be Rich Last Sunday.* Begin by choosing the characters that will be part of your ending. Then make sure that your ending follows the events of the beginning and middle of the story. Use adjectives to describe what happens.

Responses will vary but the new ending should follow

the correct sequence and should include adjectives.

Conventions

Expanding Simple Sentences Rewrite the sentences below by adding an adjective.

1. I found a penny on the sidewalk.

Example: I found a new penny on the sidewalk.

2. My family bought a chair.

Example: My family bought a soft chair.

3. He saw a spider.

Example: He saw a huge spider.

Children write routinely for a range of tasks, purposes, and audiences. Children practice various conventions of standard English.

Name _____

DIRECTIONS Write sentences using the words below.

absolutely vanish

Responses should show contextual understanding of

the words.

Copyright © Pearson Education, Inc., or its affiliates. All Rights Reserved.

> **Write in Response to Reading**

DIRECTIONS Revisit pp. 19–25 of _Alexander, Who Used to Be Rich Last Sunday_. Write an opinion about the way Alexander spent his money. Use details from the text to support your answer.

Responses will vary but might include that he

spent his money foolishly by renting a snake and

buying junk.

 Children demonstrate contextual understanding of Benchmark Vocabulary. Children read text closely and use text evidence in their written answers.

Name _____

DIRECTIONS Reread pp. 19–25 of *Alexander, Who Used to Be Rich Last Sunday*. Think about how the main idea and key details help you to better understand the main character. Write several sentences that describe what type of character Alexander is. Use details from the text to support your answer.

Responses will vary but might include that he says he is going to save, but he doesn't. He acts before he thinks. He loses his temper when his dad fines him for saying bad words and for kicking. He is careless and loses money.

Children analyze and respond to literary and informational text.

Name _____

DIRECTIONS The book *Alexander, Who Used to Be Rich Last Sunday* does not use any dialogue. Write a dialogue between two of the characters during one of the events of the book. Make sure to use speaker tags to identify each character and to use quotation marks correctly. Revisit the text to look for ideas.

Responses will vary but dialogue should be text based.

Example: "You should be in a cage," Nick said.

"Be quiet!" shouted Alexander.

Conventions

Expanding Simple Sentences Rewrite the sentences below using adverbs. **Responses will vary.**

1. "I read my book."

 Example: "I quickly read my book."

2. She walked into the library.

 Example: She walked quietly into the library.

3. The cat purred.

 Example: The cat purred softly.

Children write routinely for a range of tasks, purposes, and audiences. Children practice various conventions of standard English.

Name _____

DIRECTIONS Write a sentence using the word below.

positively

Responses should show contextual understanding of

the word.

Write in
Response to
Reading

DIRECTIONS Revisit pp. 26–32 of *Alexander, Who Used to Be Rich Last Sunday.* Write an e-mail from Alexander's point of view to his parents, telling them what he learned. Use details from the text to support your answer.

Responses will vary, but the e-mail might indicate that

he wishes he saved his money instead of buying dumb

things.

Children demonstrate contextual understanding of Benchmark Vocabulary. Children read text closely and use text evidence in their written answers.

Name _____

DIRECTIONS Return to the dialogue you wrote in Lesson 8. Revise and edit your writing, looking for places to add or change words. Look for and correct errors in grammar, punctuation, and capitalization. Remember that adjectives and adverbs will help readers form clear and interesting pictures in their minds. Then copy your revised and edited work onto a fresh sheet of paper.

Children should revise their writing as described above.

Conventions

Compound Subjects Write sentences using the compound subjects, "Felix and Max," "The teacher and her students," and "The dog and the cat." **Responses will vary.**

1. Example: Felix and Max are best friends.

2. Example: The teacher and her students are going on a field trip.

3. Example: The dog and the cat are enemies.

Children write routinely for a range of tasks, purposes, and audiences. Children practice various conventions of standard English.

Name _____

DIRECTIONS Write sentences using the words below.

tulips block

Responses should show contextual understanding of

the words.

DIRECTIONS Revisit *A Chair for My Mother.* Do you think the illustrations help you to imagine what it would be like if your own house burned down? Use details from the text to support your answer.

Responses will vary. Example: Yes. They show Mama

and the girl running in panic and then looking at all

the charred remains.

Children demonstrate contextual understanding of Benchmark Vocabulary. Children read text closely and use text evidence in their written answers.

Name _____

DIRECTIONS Using evidence from the text, answer the following question about *A Chair for My Mother.*

1. Reread pp. 62–63 of *A Chair for My Mother.* How does the illustration support the text on p. 63? Do you think the story would be the same without the illustrations? Use examples from the text to support your answer.

Responses will vary but should include that the illustration shows the fire engines, the smoke, the orange flames, and Mama and the girl running. Although the text describes the scene, the illustration makes it more real.

Children analyze and respond to literary and informational text.

Name _____

DIRECTIONS Think back to the characters in *A Chair for My Mother.* Choose a character from the story, identify the main events, and create a Character Web to show how the character responds to those events.

Children should choose a character, identify the story's main events, and create a Character Web to show how the character responds.

Conventions

Using Verbs in Sentences Use the words below to complete each sentence.

sees walked played feeds

_____ _____

1. I _____walked_____ to the park and _____played_____ frisbee.

2. She _____sees_____ the ducks and _____feeds_____ them.

Children write routinely for a range of tasks, purposes, and audiences. Children practice various conventions of standard English.

Name _____

r-Controlled *ar, or, ore, oar*

b**oar** c**ore** f**or**k be**ar**

Pick a word from the box to match each picture.
Write the word on the line.

shark	shore	bore	thorn	score
snore	roar	cart	porch	star

1. 2. 3. 4.

roar shore thorn score

5. 6. 7. 8.

porch snore star shark

Pick a word that means the opposite of each word below.
Write the word on the line.

9. entertain bore _____

10. not carry cart _____

 Children apply grade-level phonics and word
analysis skills.

Name _____

DIRECTIONS Write sentences using the words below.

exchanged savings

Responses should show contextual understanding of

the words.

Write in Response to Reading

DIRECTIONS Write a compare and contrast statement about the plots of *Alexander, Who Used to Be Rich Last Sunday* and *A Chair for My Mother.* Use details from both texts to support your answer.

Responses might compare how characters want

something in both texts; however, only one character

achieves her goal.

Children demonstrate contextual understanding of Benchmark Vocabulary. Children read text closely and use text evidence in their written answers.

DIRECTIONS Revise your writing from Lesson 10. Add sequence words to your Character Web that expand on your characters' responses.

Children should revise their writing and add sequence words.

Compound Sentences Combine the simple sentences below using *and* or *but*.

I. The rain fell. The thunder boomed.

The rain fell, and the thunder boomed.

2. I lost my tooth. It wasn't the first one I lost.

I lost my tooth, but it wasn't the first one I lost.

Children write routinely for a range of tasks, purposes, and audiences. Children practice various conventions of standard English.

Name _____

DIRECTIONS Write a sentence using the word below.

rich

Responses should show contextual understanding of

the word.

> **Write in
> Response to
> Reading**

DIRECTIONS Write an opinion about the character you think has the better approach to money—Alexander or the girl. Use details from the texts to support your opinion.

Responses should use text evidence about how

Alexander wastes his money and how the girl earns

and saves money to conclude that the girl has the

better approach to money.

Children demonstrate contextual understanding of Benchmark Vocabulary. Children read text closely and use text evidence in their written answers.

Name _____

DIRECTIONS Review the T-Chart you created that lists Alexander's point of view and the girl's point of view in *Alexander, Who Used to Be Rich Last Sunday* and *A Chair for My Mother.* Using evidence from the text, write a comparison statement about how these two characters' points of view are similar or different. Use evidence from each text to support your answer.

Responses will vary but should use evidence from the text including the ways Alexander spends money as compared to the way the girl saves money.

Children analyze and respond to literary and informational text.

Name _____

DIRECTIONS Choose a character from one of the texts to write a narrative about. Your narrative should tell about the choices that character makes in the story. Use details from the text to support your answer.

Responses will vary but should be about a specific

character's choices.

Compound Sentences Write compound sentences that use the word *and*.

1. Responses will vary. Example: Mama is in the

 diner, and the girl is at home.

2. Responses will vary. Example: He kicks, and his

 dad is not happy.

Children write routinely for a range of tasks, purposes, and audiences. Children practice various conventions of standard English.

Name _____

DIRECTIONS Write sentences using the words below.

save bargain

Responses should show contextual understanding of the words.

Write in Response to Reading

DIRECTIONS Write several sentences about which character you like more—Alexander or the girl. What do the pictures tell you about the character you prefer? Use details from both texts to support your answer.

Responses should use text details and illustrations to tell which character is preferred.

Children demonstrate contextual understanding of Benchmark Vocabulary. Children read text closely and use text evidence in their written answers.

Name _____

More Than Cash Dispensers

Have you ever visited an ATM? Did you stare in wonder when, like magic, money came out of the machine? Several decades ago banking wasn't so convenient.

People use banks to safely keep and save money. Then, when they need to spend it, they withdraw the money. That's hard to do if your bank isn't nearby. It's even harder to do if your bank is closed. So how do you get cash when you need it?

In the early 1970s, the first ATM, or automated teller machine, was introduced. Using a plastic bank card and a PIN, or personal identification number, people could access their bank accounts. They could do this at any time of day or night or even when the bank was closed. They could withdraw money, and they could deposit money and checks. ATMs started springing up everywhere, making it easy for people to withdraw money from their bank accounts.

Banks are adding new ATM services every year. For example, people can now deposit checks without using an envelope. That's because ATMs scan, or read, checks. Another improvement is talking ATMs. These machines have audio, so people that cannot see well or at all can access their bank accounts by listening to instructions.

Children read text closely to determine wheat the text says.

Name _____

ATMs keep improving. Some ATMs now have video screens. A banker uses the video screen to talk with the person using the ATM. Other banks are even testing ways mobile phones can be used at ATMs. Just imagine what ATMs will be able to do next!

Look for Clues

Underline one piece of evidence from the text that tells how modern ATMs are different from ATMs from the early 1970s.

Ask Questions

Write a question you have about ATMs.

Example: Who invented ATMs?

Make Your Case

Underline the most convincing statement the writer makes to support the idea that ATMs are more than just cash dispensers.

Make Your Case: Extend Your Ideas

Write why you agree or disagree that ATMs are more than cash dispensers.

Responses should support the opinion.

Children read text closely to determine what the text says.

Writing

DIRECTIONS Reread the narrative writing you did in Lesson 12. Revise your narrative to make it stronger and more descriptive. Remember to include graphics or pictures in your display.

Responses should include edits to make the narrative more descriptive, and include graphics or pictures.

Conventions

Compound Sentences Write compound sentences that use the word *but*.

1. Responses will vary. Example: I am tall, but my sister is short.

2. Responses will vary. Example: He lost the bet, but he didn't want to pay.

Children write routinely for a range of tasks, purposes, and audiences. Children practice various conventions of standard English.

Name _____

Contractions

Read the contractions in the box.
Pick the contraction that is formed
from each pair of words.
Write the contraction on the line.

It <u>is</u> happy.
It<u>'s</u> happy.

can't haven't he's I'm she's they'll we'll who's

I. have + not

haven't

2. I + am

I'm

3. can + not

can't

4. they + will

they'll

5. who + is

who's

6. we + will

we'll

Circle the contraction in each sentence.

7. (He's) her little brother.

8. (She's) his big sister.

9. Lisa (hasn't) eaten lunch yet.

10. Steven (can't) hear (who's) knocking!

Children apply grade-level phonics and word
analysis skills.

Lesson 1

Name _____

Benchmark Vocabulary

DIRECTIONS Write a sentence using the word below.

spending

Responses should show contextual understanding

of the word.

Write in
Response to
Reading

DIRECTIONS Reread pp. 18–19 of *Money Matters!* Write several sentences about the main purpose of these pages. Use examples from the text to support your answer.

Responses should use text evidence to show that the

purpose is to tell the difference between credit and

debit cards. Responses might include the importance

of tracking credit card debt.

Children demonstrate contextual understanding of Benchmark Vocabulary. Children read text closely and use text evidence in their written answers.

Name _____

DIRECTIONS Write an opinion about whether or not the author of *Money Matters!* achieved her purpose of informing people about money and how it matters to people. Give reasons from the text to support your opinion.

Responses may state that, yes, the author did achieve

her purpose. Reasons include that money is a part of

everyday life, and we use it to buy things.

Conventions

Commas in a Series Write two new sentences, each using commas in a series, on the lines below.

1. Responses will vary. Example: I love dogs, cats,

and birds.

2. Responses will vary. Example: Mom, Dad, and

Aunt Nan are here.

Children write routinely for a range of tasks, purposes, and audiences. Children practice various conventions of standard English.

Name _____

DIRECTIONS Write sentences using the words below.

earn choices

Responses should show contextual understanding of

the words.

Write in Response to Reading

DIRECTIONS Reread p. 6 of *Money Matters!* When do you think it is appropriate to make a trade? Use the text to support your answer.

Responses will vary but should include text evidence

about trading when we have no money. Friends

might trade toys they no longer want.

Children demonstrate contextual understanding of Benchmark Vocabulary. Children read text closely and use text evidence in their written answers.

DIRECTIONS Using evidence from the text, answer the following questions about pp. 4–9 of *Money Matters!*

1. Reread the first paragraph on p. 6 of *Money Matters!* Write several sentences about how the information on that page relates to the main topic. Use examples from the text to support your answer.

Responses will vary but should include evidence

that tells what to do if you have no money, which is

important to the main topic.

2. Reread p. 9 of *Money Matters!* What items have been used as currency in the past?

shells, blankets, goats, rice, cacao seeds, salt,

squirrel skins, rings

3. Which item of currency most surprises you?

Responses should include one item and why.

Children analyze and respond to literary and informational text.

Name _____

DIRECTIONS Write a paragraph about why you think it is important to make good decisions. Remember to use the answers to your three questions, as well as the ideas you discussed with your partner.

Responses use the answers to the three questions to tell why it is important to make good decisions.

Conventions

Commas in Compound Sentences Write two of your own compound sentences using commas.

1. Responses will vary. Example: Joe leads, and Bill follows.

2. Responses will vary. Example: Mom is nice, and Dad is too.

Children write routinely for a range of tasks, purposes, and audiences. Children practice various conventions of standard English.

Name _____

DIRECTIONS Write sentences using the words below.

agree valuable refuse

Responses should show contextual understanding of

the words.

Write in Response to Reading

DIRECTIONS Reread p. 13 of *Money Matters!* What is a gold rush? How do you know? Use examples from the text to support your answer.

A gold rush happens when gold is found, and people

rush to that place. A gold rush happened in 1896.

Children demonstrate contextual understanding of Benchmark Vocabulary. Children read text closely and use text evidence in their written answers.

Name _____

DIRECTIONS Using evidence from the text, answer the following questions about pp. 10–15 of *Money Matters!*

1. Reread pp. 12–13. How do the text features on these pages help you locate key facts?

 <u>Responses should address how the text features</u>

 <u>add to understanding the key ideas.</u>

2. Reread pp. 14–15. How do the text features on these pages help you locate key facts?

 <u>Responses should address how the text features</u>

 <u>add to understanding the key ideas.</u>

3. What is counterfeit money? Use examples from the text to support your answer.

 <u>Criminals copy official money, and the fake money</u>

 <u>is called counterfeit money.</u>

Children analyze and respond to literary and informational text.

Name _____

DIRECTIONS Write an opinion about the section of text you think is most helpful for your life. Remember to state your opinion clearly, include reasons to support your opinion, and to include at least one compound sentence that uses a comma.

Responses will vary but should include an opinion,

reasons to support the opinion, and one compound

sentence.

Conventions

Commas in Compound Sentences Write two of your own compound sentences using commas.

1. **Responses will vary. Example: Mike is my pal, and**

Jim is his pal.

2. **Responses will vary. Example: The ball is here,**

and the bat is there.

 Children write routinely for a range of tasks, purposes, and audiences. Children practice various conventions of standard English.

Name _____

DIRECTIONS Write sentences using the words below.

sold borrow bought

Responses should show contextual understanding of

the words.

Write in
Response to
Reading

DIRECTIONS Reread pp. 16–17 of *Money Matters!* Why are banks a safe place to store money? Use examples from the text to support your answer.

Responses will vary. Example: Banks store, track, and

lend money. Banks are a safe place, perhaps because

of tight security.

Children demonstrate contextual understanding of Benchmark Vocabulary. Children read text closely and use text evidence in their written answers.

Name _____

DIRECTIONS Using evidence from the text, answer the following questions about pp. 16–19 of *Money Matters!*

1. Reread p. 17. What are debit and credit cards normally used for?

People use the cards to pay for goods.

2. Reread pp. 18–19. What is a credit card?

A credit card lets people borrow money without

visiting the bank.

3. How is a credit card different from cash?

People buy goods without carrying money. When

you use the card, you are borrowing money.

4. Why is it important to track how much you spend if you're using a credit card?

It's important so you don't overspend.

Children analyze and respond to literary and informational text.

DIRECTIONS Write an opinion about whether you would use a debit or a credit card if you could. Remember to support your opinion with reasons. Use examples from the text to support your answer.

Responses should include an

opinion supported by text-based

reasons.

Conventions

Commas in Dates Add a comma to the dates below.

1. February 20 1990

February 20, 1990

2. December 21 1986

December 21, 1986

3. August 10 2005

August 10, 2005

Children write routinely for a range of tasks, purposes, and audiences. Children practice various conventions of standard English.

Benchmark Vocabulary

DIRECTIONS Write sentences using the words below.

services measures useful

Responses should show contextual understanding of the words.

Write in
Response to
Reading

DIRECTIONS Reread pp. 24–25 of *Money Matters!* What text features help you to understand what an entrepreneur is? Use examples from the text to support your answer.

Each photo and caption tell about a young

entrepreneur who started his or her own business.

Example: Fraser Doherty started selling jam at age 14.

Children demonstrate contextual understanding of Benchmark Vocabulary. Children read text closely and use text evidence in their written answers.

Name _____

DIRECTIONS Write a paragraph that tells about two questions you asked that were answered on pp. 22–25 of *Money Matters!.* Use evidence from the text. What text features helped you answer these questions?

Responses will vary but should include text-based answers to two questions that the child asked before reading the pages.

Children analyze and respond to literary and informational text.

Name _____

DIRECTIONS Revisit a section of *Money Matters!* and write a sentence about its purpose. Include a description about the section's text features and the information it provides to readers. Then include an opinion about whether the text features helped support the author's purpose.

Responses should include the purpose of a section

with a description of its text features, and an opinion

about whether the text features support the purpose.

Conventions

Commas and Adjectives Write two sentences using the adjective pairs below. Remember to use commas.

1. fuzzy pink **2.** tiny green

1. Responses will vary. Example: I have fuzzy, pink

slippers.

2. Responses will vary. Example: The tiny, green

bug scares me.

Children write routinely for a range of tasks, purposes, and audiences. Children practice various conventions of standard English.

Name _____

r-Controlled *er, ir, ur*

f**er**n b**ir**d s**ur**f

Read the words. **Circle** the correct word for each picture.

1.

(turtle) torn

2.

short (shirt)

3.

(herd) hard

4.

nose (nurse)

Look at the first word. **Circle** the word in the sentence that has the same vowel sound as the first word.

her	**5.** I live around the (corner) from Amy.
burn	**6.** My mom puts her keys in her (purse).
dirt	**7.** Liam was the (first) in line for lunch.
perch	**8.** We like to watch (monster) movies.

Children apply grade-level phonics and word analysis skills.

Name _____

DIRECTIONS Write sentences using the words below.

skills chores

Responses should show contextual understanding of

the words.

> Write in
> Response to
> Reading

DIRECTIONS Reread pp. 28–29 of *Money Matters!* Why do you think it's important to budget? Use examples from the text to support your answer.

Responses should use text evidence to show

budgeting is important because it helps you save and

spend money sensibly.

Children demonstrate contextual understanding of Benchmark Vocabulary. Children read text closely and use text evidence in their written answers.

DIRECTIONS Write an opinion about what you think is more valuable—things or experiences? Use conjunctions to connect your reasons and points. Use examples from the text to support your answer.

Responses should include an opinion as to which is

more valuable, use conjunctions, and use examples

from the text to support the opinion.

Conventions

Commas Circle any sentence that uses commas correctly. Cross out any sentence that does not use commas correctly.

1. ~~The tree branch fell and it landed, on my face.~~

2. (I like credit cards because they're tiny, reliable, and secure.)

3. ~~Money can't buy you happiness, It can't help you live forever either.~~

Children write routinely for a range of tasks, purposes, and audiences. Children practice various conventions of standard English.

Name _____

DIRECTIONS Write sentences using the words below.

doubt compassionate

Responses should show contextual understanding of the words.

Write in Response to Reading

DIRECTIONS Write two questions you would want to ask Alex from the story *I Wanna Iguana*. Revisit the text to help you.

Responses will vary. Examples:

Are you sure you want to clean an iguana's cage?

How much lettuce does it eat?

Children demonstrate contextual understanding of Benchmark Vocabulary. Children read text closely and use text evidence in their written answers.

Name _____

DIRECTIONS Reread pp. 84–85 of *I Wanna Iguana*. Think about questions you find yourself asking as you read. Write your questions down, and then write the answers to your questions.

Responses will vary but should include logical questions and correct answers. Example question: What is that brown thing in the art on the page? Example answer: The text is about tarantulas, so that must be a picture of one.

Children analyze and respond to literary and informational text.

Name _____

DIRECTIONS Revisit the opinion paragraph you wrote in Lesson 6. Revise your paragraph by adding additional reasons that support your opinion. Then add linking words or phrases to further strengthen your paragraph.

Responses should include edits to the paragraph

by adding additional reasons and linking words or

phrases.

Commas in Letters How would you start a letter to a friend? Write your greeting on the lines below. Then write a short letter of your own to a friend. Responses will vary.

Greeting: Example: Dear Cara,

I miss you. Please come visit!

Your friend,

Nicky

Children write routinely for a range of tasks, purposes, and audiences. Children practice various conventions of standard English.

Name _____

DIRECTIONS Write sentences using the words below.

mention concerned

Responses should show contextual understanding of the words.

DIRECTIONS Many stories include dialogue, but *I Wanna Iguana* is told through a series of letters. Do you think the story would be better if it had dialogue?

Responses might include an opinion that the story was funnier when told through the letters.

Children demonstrate contextual understanding of Benchmark Vocabulary. Children read text closely and use text evidence in their written answers.

Name _____

Another Movie Night to Remember

For weeks, I had seen a big, red circle on the calendar. It was my parents' anniversary. I got the sense this was an important day, and I wanted to do something to celebrate . . . but what?

Mom had once told us that Dad asked her to marry him after taking her out for pizza and a romantic movie. We decided to have a movie night that Mom and Dad would never forget.

We bought the ingredients to make Mom's favorite pizza. My older sister Bethany found out what movie they had seen, and we rented it for the night. But everything started to go wrong.

First, the pizza slid off the pan and onto the floor as I carried it to the table. Next, Bethany burned the popcorn, so the whole house smelled awful. Then we discovered that the DVD wouldn't play. Bethany and I were upset, but Dad chuckled as he opened a window to air out the house. He took us out to dinner, to the same restaurant where he and Mom had eaten that special night. Over pizza, we heard the story of how Mom and Dad met. It was better than the best romantic movie—even without popcorn!

Children read text closely to determine what the text says.

Look for Clues

Underline details that support the idea that Mom and Dad were not upset about the problems that happened with the surprise.

Ask Questions

On a separate piece of paper, write a question that you would ask someone who is celebrating a special day.

Responses might ask what the person wants to do on this day.

Ask Questions: Extend Your Ideas

What questions would you ask the girls who planned the event?

Responses might include asking how the pizza fell.

Make Your Case

Write three words or phrases that describe the narrator's feelings. Then, on a separate piece of paper, write a new version of the story, using your own words.

Children write the three words they selected.

Make Your Case: Extend Your Ideas

Do you think it was smart for the girls to plan a surprise for their parents? On a separate piece of paper, write an opinion about this.

Responses should give an opinion with reasons.

Children read text closely to determine what the text says.

Name _____

DIRECTIONS Choose a letter from Mom on pp. 81–87 in *I Wanna Iguana*. Then, on a separate sheet of paper, rewrite one of Alex's responses to that letter. Give different reasons to support the opinion you express in the letter. Make sure to list facts or reasons in your letter. Choose your words carefully to persuade Alex's mom to accept your opinion. Remember to use commas correctly in both the greeting and closing of your letter.

Responses should include a rewrite of one letter, with commas used correctly.

Commas in Letters How would you finish a letter to a friend? Write your closing on the lines below. Remember to use commas correctly.

Responses should include a closing to a letter, with commas used correctly.

Children write routinely for a range of tasks, purposes, and audiences. Children practice various conventions of standard English.

Unit 2 • Module B • Lesson 8 • 141

Name _____

DIRECTIONS Write a sentence using the word below.

exactly

Responses should show contextual understanding of the word.

DIRECTIONS Reread pp. 91–92 of _I Wanna Iguana._ What do you know about Alex's father? Do you think he is more like his wife or Alex? Write a few sentences that explain your opinion. Use details from the text to support your opinion.

Responses should include an opinion about Alex's father, with reasons to support the opinion.

Children demonstrate contextual understanding of Benchmark Vocabulary. Children read text closely and use text evidence in their written answers.

Name _____

Reread pp. 88–95 of *I Wanna Iguana.* Choose a character from the text and list some of his or her traits on the lines below. Then write several sentences about the character you chose. Why do you like him or her? Use examples from the text to support your answer. **Responses will vary.**

Character: **Example: Alex.** _____

Trait 1: **Example: persistent** _____

Trait 2: **Example: clever** _____

Trait 3: **Example: funny** _____

Why?: **Example: I like Alex because he never gives up.**

He thinks of clever and funny reasons to give to his

mother.

Children analyze and respond to literary and informational text.

Name _____

DIRECTIONS Review pages 88–95 in *I Wanna Iguana.* Look at the details the author uses to describe Alex's character. On a separate piece of paper, write a letter to Alex's mom as if you were a friend of Alex. Tell Alex's mom whether you think he should have the iguana or not. Make sure to give reasons that support your opinion.

Responses include a letter to Alex's mom from Alex's friend, stating reasons whether Alex should have the iguana.

Conventions

Commas in Letters Write the greetings below correctly.

1. Dear Uncle Mike

Dear Uncle Mike,

2. Dear, Mom

Dear Mom,

Children write routinely for a range of tasks, purposes, and audiences. Children practice various conventions of standard English.

DIRECTIONS Write sentences using the words below.

responsible financial

Responses should show contextual understanding of

the words.

Write in
Response to
Reading

DIRECTIONS Write a few sentences to answer this question: Do you think Alex will take care of the iguana and be able to keep it? Use details from the text to support your answer.

Responses should include details to support the

opinion. Example: Alex let the fish jump into the

spaghetti, so he may not be responsible enough to

care for a pet.

Children demonstrate contextual understanding of Benchmark Vocabulary. Children read text closely and use text evidence in their written answers.

DIRECTIONS Using evidence from the text, answer the following questions about pp. 84–85 of *I Wanna Iguana.*

1. Reread p. 84. Is more than one point of view expressed on this page?

 Yes, Alex's and his mother's points of view are

 expressed.

2. How do the text features on these pages help you figure out point of view?

 Responses might include how the letters share

 the points of view of Alex and his mom.

3. Reread pp. 84–85. How is Alex's point of view different from his mom's?

 Responses will vary. Example: Alex thinks

 iguanas are cute, but his mom does not.

Children analyze and respond to literary and informational text.

Name _____

DIRECTIONS Think about what you have read in *I Wanna Iguana.* Decide whether you agree with Alex or his mom's point of view about having an iguana as a pet. Use details and reasons from the text to support your opinion.

Responses will vary but should include evidence from the text to support the opinion.

Conventions

Use Commas Circle the closing that is correct. Then write your own short letter on the lines below.

I. (Sincerely, Mackenzie) Sincerely Mackenzie

2. Responses should include a letter that is correctly punctuated.

Children write routinely for a range of tasks, purposes, and audiences. Children practice various conventions of standard English.

Lesson 11

Name _____

r-Controlled *er, ir, ur*

Read the words. **Write** the word for each picture.

1.

2.

3.

4.

Look at the first word. **Circle** the word in the sentence that has the same vowel sound as the first word.

nurse 5. The man at the store found my mother's (purse) and returned it to her.

squirt 6. I was playing tag on the playground when my (shirt) ripped.

hamster 7. My dog likes to sit (under) the table.

birthday 8. Yesterday was the (first) time I ate a banana split!

Children apply grade-level phonics and word analysis skills.

DIRECTIONS Write sentences using the words below.

chores allowance

Responses should show contextual understanding of

the words.

DIRECTIONS Reread p. 93 of _I Wanna Iguana_ and pp. 26–27 of _Money Matters!_ What do these two sections have in common? Use details from both texts to support your answer.

Both texts refer to an allowance. One text says that

sometimes parents give children money each week,

which is an allowance; Alex writes about using his

allowance to buy lettuce.

Children demonstrate contextual understanding of
Benchmark Vocabulary. Children read text closely and
use text evidence in their written answers.

Name _____

DIRECTIONS Reread the text on pp. 26–27 of *Money Matters!* and p. 93 of *I Wanna Iguana.* Write a paragraph about how you would spend your money. Use examples and details from the text to support your opinion.

Responses should include ways that tell how the child

would spend money, perhaps by helping to pay for a

pet's food, as Alex said he would do.

Conventions

Simple Sentences Complete each sentence below to include the missing subject or predicate.

Responses will vary.

1. Example: Alex _____ wrote a letter to his mom.

2. The family Example: likes the pet _____.

Children write routinely for a range of tasks, purposes, and audiences. Children practice various conventions of standard English.

Name _____

DIRECTIONS Write a sentence using the word below.

need

Responses should show contextual understanding of the word.

Write in Response to Reading

DIRECTIONS Think back to the two texts—*I Wanna Iguana* and *Money Matters!* Which text do you think gets its message across more clearly? Use details from the text to support your opinion.

Responses will vary but should use text evidence to support an opinion.

 Children demonstrate contextual understanding of Benchmark Vocabulary. Children read text closely and use text evidence in their written answers.

Name _____

DIRECTIONS Think back to the main topic and author's message in *I Wanna Iguana* and *Money Matters!* Write several sentences that compare and contrast the main topic of each book. Remember to include details from both texts to support your answer.

I Wanna Iguana:

Responses should use text evidence to state that the

main topic is Alex's desire for a pet iguana. This is a

fictional story written to entertain the reader.

Money Matters!:

Responses should use text evidence to state that the

main topic is the importance of money in people's

lives. The author's purpose is to inform.

Children analyze and respond to literary and informational text.

Name _____

DIRECTIONS Revise your opinion piece about using your own money wisely. Expand your writing using reasons and evidence from the text and your own opinions about handling money. Remember that you can strengthen your message by including details and examples.

Responses should include text evidence to support

opinions about using money wisely.

Conventions

Expanding Simple Sentences Add or change words to expand the simple sentences below. **Responses will vary.**

1. My family needs a budget.

Example: My entire family is on a strict budget.

2. Do you have a lot of coins?

Example: Do you have a lot of rare, old coins?

 Children write routinely for a range of tasks, purposes, and audiences. Children practice various conventions of standard English.

Name _____

Plurals

Write the word for each picture. **Use** the words in the box to help you.

Add -s, -es, change the **y** to **i** and add **-es,** or change the **f** to **v** and add **-es.**

bunny	bush	calf	fork	fox
house	leaf	candy	shelf	spoon

1.

forks

2.

houses

3.

bushes

4.

candies

5.

bunnies

6.

calves

7.

foxes

8.

spoons

9.

leaves

10.

shelves

 Children apply grade-level phonics and word analysis skills.

Name _____

DIRECTIONS Write sentences using the words below.

unusual energy

Responses should show contextual understanding of the words.

Write in Response to Reading

DIRECTIONS Reread pp. 1–9 of *Theodore Roosevelt: The Adventurous President.* Think about the subheadings found throughout the section. What was Teddy Roosevelt like as a child? What subheading helps you to answer this question?

"A Sickly Kid" tells that when Teddy wasn't sick, he was full of energy and was always moving.

Children demonstrate contextual understanding of Benchmark Vocabulary. Children read text closely and use text evidence in their written answers.

Name _____

Writing

DIRECTIONS Think about Chapters 1 and 2 of *Theodore Roosevelt: The Adventurous President*. Write a few sentences about something you have learned and explain how it applies to your life.

Responses will vary but should use evidence from

the text to indicate what the child learned.

Conventions

Capitalizing Geographic Names Rewrite the correct geographical names on the lines below. Then write your own sentence using a capitalized geographical name correctly.

1. I live in the city of chicago. Chicago

2. My older sister traveled to shanghai with her friends.

Shanghai

3. Sentence includes a geographical name spelled correctly.

Children write routinely for a range of tasks, purposes, and audiences. Children practice various conventions of standard English.

Name _____

DIRECTIONS Write sentences using the words below.

honor politics

Responses should show contextual understanding of the words.

Write in Response to Reading

DIRECTIONS Think about Chapters 3, 4, and 5 of *Theodore Roosevelt: The Adventurous President*. Write several sentences about your opinion of Theodore Roosevelt so far. Use details from the text to support your answer.

Responses will vary but should use text evidence from the chapters to support the opinion.

Children demonstrate contextual understanding of Benchmark Vocabulary. Children read text closely and use text evidence in their written answers.

DIRECTIONS Using evidence from *Theodore Roosevelt: The Adventurous President,* follow the directions below.

1. Think back to today's reading. Write one unanswered question that you asked while reading.

<u>The question should be about the day's reading.</u>

2. Tell how you might find the answer to that question.

<u>Response might suggest by looking on the Internet.</u>

3. Write one question that you asked that was answered by the text.

<u>The question is one answered in the reading.</u>

4. Write the answer to that question.

<u>Response should answer the question asked in the</u>

<u>third item.</u>

Children analyze and respond to literary and informational text.

DIRECTIONS Revisit the first few chapters of *Theodore Roosevelt: The Adventurous President*. Write down two ways that Teddy Roosevelt was building ideas for his family, New York City, and his country. Use details from the text to support your answer.

Responses might include that he set goals; he

believed people should get jobs only if they were

good at them; he was a conservationist.

Conventions

Capitalizing Geographic Names Rewrite the correct states and regions on the lines below. Then write your own sentence using a capitalized geographical name correctly.

1. My grandma moved to richmond. Richmond

2. We studied the state of new york last week.

New York

3. The sentence includes a geographical location.

Children write routinely for a range of tasks, purposes, and audiences. Children practice various conventions of standard English.

Unit 3 • Module A • Lesson 2 • 159

DIRECTIONS Write sentences using the words below.

popular strike

Responses should show contextual understanding of

the words.

DIRECTIONS Revisit Chapter 6 of *Theodore Roosevelt: The Adventurous President*. Choose a photo and write one or two sentences about what the photo tells you. Use details to support your answer.

Responses should be about a photo in the chapter.

Example: Roosevelt lived in a time before radio and

television. Most reporters were men.

Children demonstrate contextual understanding of Benchmark Vocabulary. Children read text closely and use text evidence in their written answers.

Gregor Mendel

Gregor Mendel always loved nature. He grew up on a farm. He walked through the countryside every day. He loved to look at plants and animals along the way. He noticed the ways plants are alike and different. Later, Mendel became a teacher and scientist.

One day Mendel took a long walk. He saw a flower that was different from others of the same kind. It made him wonder. What caused such differences? He began to grow pea plants as part of an experiment. In seven years, he grew thousands of plants! He kept track of different traits in plants. He noticed the color of the flowers and pea pods. He measured the height of the plants.

He noticed the shape of their pods and leaves. He saw that there was a pattern. "Parent" plants passed traits to "daughter" plants in certain ways. Mendel's studies helped him discover rules about how traits are passed on. This was the beginning of a branch of science called genetics.

Genetics has helped scientists and doctors understand more about all living things. Scientists can fight disease and grow healthier food. Next time you are curious about something, explore it! Who knows? You, like Gregor Mendel, could change the world.

Children read text closely to determine what the text says.

Look for Clues

Underline details that tell what made Mendel a good scientist.

Ask Questions

Write a question that was not answered about Mendel in the text.

Example: Where did Mendel live?

Ask Questions: Extend Your Ideas

Write a question that a reporter might ask Mendel about his research. Use the text to formulate your question. Then underline the text that Mendel would use to answer the question.

Response should include a question and an answer.

Make Your Case

Circle three facts in the text that tell about Mendel's life. Then write one fact you would like to know about him.

Children should write one fact they want to know.

Children read text closely to determine whak the text says.

Name _____

DIRECTIONS Create an idea for a new text feature to add to *Theodore Roosevelt: The Adventurous President*. What is it? Where will it go? What information will it tell? Explain how the text feature you create will support the text.

Responses should include a text feature, where it

goes, what information it adds, and how it supports

the text. Example: Insert a map in "Teddy's Great

Plans" that shows the ships' route.

Conventions

Capitalizing Geographic Names Rewrite the correct country names on the lines below. Then write your own sentence using a capitalized geographical name correctly.

I. Tanya is from mexico. _____
Mexico

2. Beijing is a major city in china. _____
China

3. _____
The sentence includes a geographical name.

Children write routinely for a range of tasks, purposes, and audiences. Children practice various conventions of standard English.

Unit 3 • Module A • Lesson 3 • 163

DIRECTIONS Write sentences using the words below.

experts extinct

Responses should show contextual understanding of

the words.

Write in
Response to
Reading

DIRECTIONS Revisit Chapters 7–8 of *Theodore Roosevelt: The Adventurous President*. Write a few sentences that tell about how Teddy and his family were affected by the three wars that occurred during his lifetime. Use details from the text to support your answer.

Teddy's dad paid another man to fight in his

place during the Civil War; Teddy was in the

Spanish-American War; his sons fought in WW1,

and one was killed.

Children demonstrate contextual understanding of Benchmark Vocabulary. Children read text closely and use text evidence in their written answers.

Name _____

DIRECTIONS Using evidence from the text, answer the following questions about Chapters 1–8 of *Theodore Roosevelt: The Adventurous President*.

1. List three major historical events that occurred during Teddy Roosevelt's lifetime:

Responses should use text evidence to list three

major events.

2. Pick one of the historical events above and tell how it affected Teddy Roosevelt's life.

Responses should use text evidence to tell how

one event affected his life.

3. Revisit pp. 10–12. Why does Teddy decide to go into politics? Use details to support your answer.

Teddy wished to please Alice, honor his father,

improve the world, and honor his family.

Children analyze and respond to literary and informational text.

DIRECTIONS Look through *Theodore Roosevelt: The Adventurous President.* Write about an event that shows Teddy Roosevelt was a creator of ideas or made contributions to the country. Use details from the text to support your answer.

Responses should include an event that shows

how Teddy was a creator of ideas, or how he made

contributions to the country.

Conventions

Capitalizing Geographic Names Correctly capitalize the continents in the sentences below. Then write your own sentence using a capitalized geographical name correctly.

1. Teddy often went hunting in africa. Africa

2. I cannot wait to travel to asia next summer! Asia

3. The sentence has a geographical name.

Children write routinely for a range of tasks, purposes, and audiences. Children practice various conventions of standard English.

Name _____

DIRECTIONS Write sentences using the words below.

grateful conservation

Responses should show contextual understanding of

the words.

DIRECTIONS Write three questions that you would ask Teddy Roosevelt or Charles Markis, who was interviewed about Roosevelt.

Responses should include three questions to either

man. Examples: What do you do at Sagamore Hill?

How long have you worked there? How many people

visit each day?

Children demonstrate contextual understanding of
Benchmark Vocabulary. Children read text closely
and use text evidence in their written answers.

Name _____

DIRECTIONS Using evidence from the text, answer the following questions about pp. 42–44 of *Theodore Roosevelt: The Adventurous President.*

1. List three words that helped you find key details about Teddy Roosevelt in the interview.

Examples: *grateful, conservation,* **and** *achievement*

2. How many acres of land did Teddy Roosevelt set aside during his presidency?

230 million acres

3. Have other presidents followed Teddy's example?

Teddy set an example for every president.

4. Write several sentences about why you think it's important to protect wilderness areas. Use details from the text to support your answer.

Responses will vary but should include reasons to

protect wilderness areas.

Children analyze and respond to literary and informational text.

Name _____

DIRECTIONS Pick a topic that you would like to know more about. Then list three questions you would like to research about that topic, and tell why you are interested in those questions.

Responses should include a topic, three questions

about the topic, and a reason why the child wants to

learn more about the topic.

Conventions

Proper Nouns Capitalize the national parks in the sentences below. Then write your own sentence using a capitalized geographical name correctly.

1. We hiked in yellowstone. Yellowstone

2. After reading about Teddy Roosevelt, I traveled to sagamore hill. Sagamore Hill

3. The sentence has a geographical name.

Children write routinely for a range of tasks, purposes, and audiences. Children practice various conventions of standard English.

Name _____

Long *a* Spelled *a, ai, ay*

Read each sentence.

Write the word with the **long *a*** sound on the line below.

<u>tail</u> tray

1. The ducklings play in the water.

play

2. The baby ducks do not see the cat.

baby

3. It is waiting in the grass.

waiting

4. The big ducks are not afraid of the cat.

afraid

5. The cat runs away as fast as it can.

away

6. We bought a new table.

table

Children apply grade-level phonics and word analysis skills.

Benchmark Vocabulary

DIRECTIONS Write sentences using the words below.

preserve proverb

Responses should show contextual understanding of

the words.

Write in
Response to
Reading

DIRECTIONS Reread the sidebars on pp. 8, 19, 30–31, 37, and 40 in *Theodore Roosevelt: The Adventurous President*. Then write a sentence or two that tells about the sidebar you find most interesting. Use details from the text to support your answer.

Responses will vary but should include a sentence

about why one sidebar is the most interesting.

Children demonstrate contextual understanding of Benchmark Vocabulary. Children read text closely and use text evidence in their written answers.

DIRECTIONS Choose a topic from the brainstorm and create a quotation that Roosevelt would have said or believed. Then explain how the quotation fits with his actions.

Responses should include one topic, a quotation that

Roosevelt would have said about the selected topic,

and how the quotation fits with Roosevelt's actions.

Adjectives Circle the adjectives in the sentences below. Then write 5 adjectives that describe your bedroom.

I. Our family hiked the (rugged) trail. We often had to stop to wait for my (little) sister to catch up. She constantly fell behind us. It really was a (long, hot) hike.

2. Responses will vary. Examples: *messy, tiny, cool,*

clean, pink

Children write routinely for a range of tasks, purposes, and audiences. Children practice various conventions of standard English.

Name _____

DIRECTIONS Write a sentence using the word below.

weary

Responses should show contextual understanding of

the word.

Write in Response to Reading

DIRECTIONS Think about the details the poet included about Abraham Lincoln's life. Then look at the illustration. Why do you think the poet chose to focus on Lincoln's childhood?

Responses will vary. Example: The poet wanted the

poem to appeal to children; she wanted to explain

what Lincoln was like as a boy.

Children demonstrate contextual understanding of Benchmark Vocabulary. Children read text closely and use text evidence in their written answers.

Name _____

DIRECTIONS Make a list of the rhyming words you found in the second, third, and fourth stanzas in "Lincoln" on pp. 166–167.

Stanza Two:

ways, blaze

stem, them

Stanza Three:

face, place

gloom, room

Stanza Four:

will, still

to-day, stay

Children analyze and respond to literary and informational text.

Name _____

DIRECTIONS Write three questions that you might want to research about Abraham Lincoln's life. Research one of the questions. Then write a paragraph that provides the answer to that question.

Responses include three questions to research, with

a paragraph providing the answer to one question.

Conventions

Adverbs Write your own sentences using adverbs that describe *how*, *when*, and *where*.

1. Sentence has an adverb that describes how.

2. Sentence has an adverb that describes when.

3. Sentence has an adverb that describes where.

Children write routinely for a range of tasks, purposes, and audiences. Children practice various conventions of standard English.

Lesson 8

Name _____

DIRECTIONS Write sentences using the words below.

rights strenuous swarmed

Responses should show contextual understanding of the words.

Write in Response to Reading

DIRECTIONS Reread pp. 103–109 of *Marching with Aunt Susan*. Based on what you have read so far, write your opinion of Bessie and her brothers. Use details from the text to support your answer.

Responses will vary, but opinions should be supported with details. Example: Bessie is quick to judge Miss Anthony based on one photo.

Children demonstrate contextual understanding of Benchmark Vocabulary. Children read text closely and use text evidence in their written answers.

Name _____

DIRECTIONS Reread pp. 106–109 of *Marching with Aunt Susan*. Write one question that you asked yourself while you read these pages. Then write the answer to that question. Use details from the text to support your answer.

Responses will vary but should include one question the reader asked, such as, "What is the meaning of the word *suffrage*?" The reader learns that it relates to the right to vote.

Children analyze and respond to literary and informational text.

Name _____

DIRECTIONS Identify the time period of *Marching with Aunt Susan.* Write three questions about that time period. Then list three sources you might use to find more information about the time period.

We know the time period was long ago by looking

at the clothing and by reading that women did not

have the right to vote. The child should provide three

relevant questions and three credible sources.

Adverbs Write your own sentences using adverbs.

1. _Responses will vary but will have an adverb in_

2. _each sentence. Examples: softly, happily, clearly_

3.

Children write routinely for a range of tasks, purposes, and audiences. Children practice various conventions of standard English.

Name _____

DIRECTIONS Write sentences using the words below.

mount balance wobbling

Responses should show contextual understanding of

the words.

Write in Response to Reading

DIRECTIONS Reread pp. 120–131 of _Marching with Aunt Susan_. Name one part of the story that is probably made up. Then name one part of the story that is probably true. Use examples from the text to support your answer.

Responses will vary but should use text evidence.

Example: The dialogue is probably made up; the part

about voting is probably true.

Children demonstrate contextual understanding of Benchmark Vocabulary. Children read text closely and use text evidence in their written answers.

Name _____

DIRECTIONS Research Susan B. Anthony. Then write a paragraph that tells your opinion of Susan B. Anthony and what she did in her life. Use examples from your research and the text to support your answer.

Responses include an opinion with supporting

examples. Example: She worked tirelessly. Research

indicates she worked 60 years for suffrage.

Conventions

Adjectives and Adverbs Write sentences that use adjectives and adverbs. Circle the adjectives and underline the adverbs.

1. Responses will vary but should include

2. sentences with circled adjectives, underlined

3. adverbs, or both.

Children write routinely for a range of tasks, purposes, and audiences. Children practice various conventions of standard English.

DIRECTIONS Write sentences using the words below.

avid portrait

Responses should show contextual understanding of

the words.

Write in
Response to
Reading

DIRECTIONS Reread pp. 132–135 of *Marching with Aunt Susan*. Do you think the author did a good job connecting Bessie's life with Susan B. Anthony? Use details from the text to support your answer.

Responses should include evidence to support the

opinion. Example: Yes. She described finding a letter

from Anthony in a box of Bessie's.

Children demonstrate contextual understanding of Benchmark Vocabulary. Children read text closely and use text evidence in their written answers.

Name _____

DIRECTIONS Review the Story Sequence graphic organizer that tells the sequence of the historical events in *Marching with Aunt Susan*. What historical event occurred after the election? Write several sentences that tell about that event.

Responses will vary but might include that after the vote was taken and the women lost, suffragists continued the fight until suffrage was approved.

Children analyze and respond to literary and informational text.

DIRECTIONS Review the Author's Note in *Marching with Aunt Susan*. Write a paragraph that explains a connection between the characters or events in the story, and something mentioned in the Author's Note. Use facts from both the note and the story to explain the connection. Include a concluding sentence that restates the connection.

The note says that the story is based on actual events.

The march happened, Anthony said the quote on

page 111, and the song was performed at meetings.

Conventions

Adjectives and Adverbs Match the adjective or adverb with the word it describes. Then write your own sentence using an adjective or an adverb.

1. loud a. whistled

2. softly b. music

3. carefully c. painted

4. _____

The sentence uses an adjective or an adverb.

 Children write routinely for a range of tasks, purposes, and audiences. Children practice various conventions of standard English.

Name _____

Long *e* Spelled *e, ee, ea, y*

w<u>e</u> wh<u>ee</u>l l<u>ea</u>f bab<u>y</u>

These bees only fly past words with the long *e* sound.
Circle each word with the **long e** sound.
Draw a line to show the path from the bees to the tree.

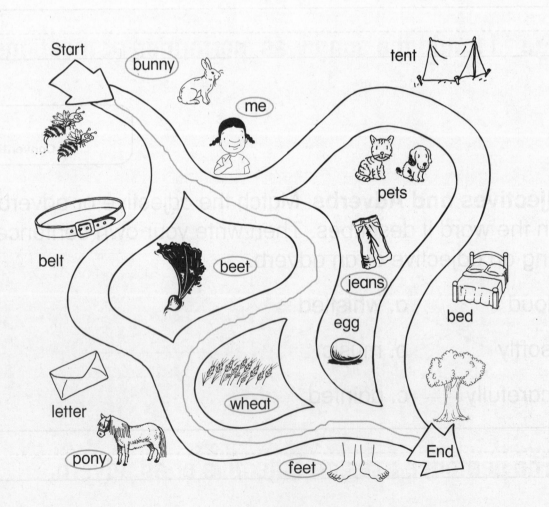

Children apply grade-level phonics and word analysis skills.

Name _____

DIRECTIONS Write sentences using the words below.

rights avid

Responses should show contextual understanding of

the words.

DIRECTIONS Think about some of the differences in the way boys and girls are thought of in this story. How have some points of view about boys and girls **not** changed since the time period of the story? Use examples to support your answer.

Responses should indicate that some people still

think that girls should not have the same privileges

as boys.

Children demonstrate contextual understanding of Benchmark Vocabulary. Children read text closely and use text evidence in their written answers.

DIRECTIONS Select someone from either text other than Teddy Roosevelt or Susan B. Anthony to research. Research that person with other classmates who chose the same person. Make a list of the resources you used for research and take notes. Then make a list of the facts you found, putting them in a logical order.

Responses will vary but should include a person's

name from either selection, a list of resources used,

and a logical list of facts.

Conventions

Expand Sentences with Adjectives Rewrite the sentences on the lines below, adding adjectives.

I. The cat chased the dog.

The sentence includes at least one adjective.

2. We spent the day at the beach.

The sentence includes at least one adjective.

Children write routinely for a range of tasks, purposes, and audiences. Children practice various conventions of standard English.

Name _____

DIRECTIONS Write sentences using the words below.

politics popular

Responses should show contextual understanding of

the words.

Write in
Response to
Reading

DIRECTIONS Which do you think is the best way to tell about a person's life—an informational text, a story, or a poem? Why? Use details from the texts to support your answer.

Responses should use evidence from the text to

support the opinion.

Children demonstrate contextual understanding of
Benchmark Vocabulary. Children read text closely
and use text evidence in their written answers.

Name _____

DIRECTIONS Using text evidence from *Theodore Roosevelt: The Adventurous President,* "Lincoln," and *Marching with Aunt Susan,* follow the directions below.

1. Write several sentences about how Abraham Lincoln, Susan B. Anthony, and Theodore Roosevelt are alike.

Responses will vary. Example: They were "strong of

will" and persistent in pursuing their goals. Roosevelt

went up against politicians, Lincoln trudged miles for

a book, and Anthony fought for women's rights.

2. Select two of the historical figures above and write several sentences about how they are different.

Responses will vary. Example: Anthony was

unsuccessful in achieving her goal, but Roosevelt

managed to stop the railroads from fixing their

prices.

Children analyze and respond to literary and informational text.

Name _____

DIRECTIONS Use the Internet to finish researching the person you chose in Lesson 11. Return to the texts *Theodore Roosevelt: The Adventurous President* and *Marching with Aunt Susan* for examples of good writing. Then, on a separate sheet of paper, write a one or two paragraph first draft about the person you chose. Use facts and details from your research to support your answer.

Responses should include one or two paragraphs about the person, including facts and details from the research.

Conventions

Expand Sentences with Adverbs Rewrite the sentences on the lines below, adding adverbs.

1. Her tooth fell out.

Responses should include an adverb.

2. The birds were singing this morning.

Responses should include an adverb.

3. My teacher led us through the Teddy Roosevelt exhibit.

Responses should include an adverb.

Children write routinely for a range of tasks, purposes, and audiences. Children practice various conventions of standard English.

Name _____

DIRECTIONS Write sentences using the words below.

unusual honor

Responses should show contextual understanding of

the words.

DIRECTIONS Think about the three texts you have read about important people in American history. Which of these texts had the strongest purpose? Why do you think so? Use evidence from the text to support your opinion.

Responses vary. Example: "Lincoln" does because

the author's word choices, such as *earnest* and *wise*

in *woodmen's ways* paint a vivid picture.

Children demonstrate contextual understanding of Benchmark Vocabulary. Children read text closely and use text evidence in their written answers.

Name _____

A Few Good Words

It takes many skills to be President of the United States. It is hard work. It has few rewards and can take a little luck, too.

The third President of the United States was Thomas Jefferson. He once said, "I'm a great believer in luck." Abraham Lincoln explained that, "Luck is when preparation meets opportunity." Our fortieth President was Ronald Reagan. He said, "There is no limit to what a man can do if he doesn't mind who gets the credit."

These three Presidents were all different kinds of leaders. They had talents that were special.

Thomas Jefferson had many skills and helped found our country. He was born in 1743 in Virginia. He was an architect, musician, and scientist. He wrote the Declaration of Independence. This paper helped the United States become its own country.

Abraham Lincoln was born in a log cabin in Kentucky in 1809. He later moved to Illinois. He taught himself how to read and study law. As President, he helped free African Americans from slavery.

Before Ronald Reagan became President he was an actor. He was born in Illinois in 1911. He became governor of California. As President he helped make peace with other countries.

Children read text closely to determine what the text says.

Name _____

Look for Clues
Underline details in the text that you could use in a biography about one of these men.

Look for Clues: Extend Your Ideas
Choose one of the men in the text. Using clues from the text, write a sentence about the kind of man you think he was.

Responses should use evidence from the text about

one man.

Ask Questions
Write one question you still have about each president.

Responses will vary but should include one question

about each man.

Make Your Case
Compare and contrast two presidents. Tell at least one way they were alike and different.

ALIKE: _____
Responses tell how they are alike.

DIFFERENT: _____
Responses describe differences.

Children read text closely to determine what the text says.

Name _____

DIRECTIONS Revise and edit your research paper. As you rewrite, look to expand your sentences using descriptive words. Make sure you have included facts and details from your research. Remember that each paragraph should have a topic sentence, supporting details, and a concluding sentence.

Responses should include descriptive words and

facts. Each paragraph should have a topic sentence,

supporting details, and a concluding sentence.

Conventions

Expand Sentences with Adjectives and Adverbs Write your own sentences that use adjectives and adverbs.

1. Responses will vary but should include an adjective

2. or an adverb.

Children write routinely for a range of tasks, purposes, and audiences. Children practice various conventions of standard English.

Name _____

Long *e* Spelled *e, ee, ea, y*

Pick a word from the box to match each clue. Write the word on the line.
Underline the letters of the word that make the long *e* sound.

beak	bake	sheep	ship
kitty	be	bee	

1. a cat

2. a bird's bill

beak

3. wooly animals

4. a buzzing bug

bee

Read the story. **Underline** words with long *e* spelled *e, ee, ea, y.*

Dad took Bree and me to the beach. We rode in the jeep along the seashore. We parked in the lot and went to the sand. We could feel the heat of the sand on our feet. There was a lot of seaweed on the sand. At the snack bar, I got bean and cheese wraps for Bree and me. I got an iced tea for Dad. He wanted to read his book. Bree wanted to feed her beans to the seagulls. She dropped one on the sand, and a seagull snatched it in his beak. The seagulls were glad we came. So were we.

Children apply grade-level phonics and word analysis skills.

Name _____

DIRECTIONS Write sentences using the words below.

community inventor creative

Responses should show contextual understanding of

the words.

Write in
Response to
Reading

DIRECTIONS Reread p. 4 of _Change Makers_. What is the main topic of this page? Use details from the text to support your answer.

Every change starts with an idea. An example detail

is that people think of ideas to solve problems.

Children demonstrate contextual understanding of Benchmark Vocabulary. Children read text closely and use text evidence in their written answers.

Name _____

DIRECTIONS Write a paragraph that clearly states and describes the main topic of *Change Makers*. Be sure to include an explanation of how the main topic relates to the title of the unit. Use details from the text to support your answer.

Responses should tell how ideas can lead to solving

problems. The unit title is Building Ideas, which is

what happens when you solve a problem.

Conventions

Prepositions Circle the preposition in each sentence. Then write your own sentence that uses a preposition.

1. The class took a trip (to) the zoo.

2. My dad found his lost socks (under) the bed.

3. Sentences should have a preposition.

Children write routinely for a range of tasks, purposes, and audiences. Children practice various conventions of standard English.

Name _____

DIRECTIONS Write sentences using the words below.

destroyed harming products

Responses should show contextual understanding of the words.

Write in Response to Reading

DIRECTIONS Reread pp. 14–16 of *Change Makers*. What problem did Madison and Rhiannon discover? What did they do about it? Use details from the text to support your answer.

Trees were being cut down for their palm oil. The girls checked products for palm oil.

Children demonstrate contextual understanding of Benchmark Vocabulary. Children read text closely and use text evidence in their written answers.

Name _____

DIRECTIONS Using evidence from the text, answer the following questions about pp. 12–17 of *Change Makers.*

1. Reread pp. 14–16. What is the connection between Madison and Rhiannon's e-mail campaign and orangutans?

The e-mails asked for cookies to be made without

palm oil to save the trees.

2. Reread p. 17. Why does the author ask if you have products in your home that contain palm oil?

She wants you to tell companies to stop using

palm oil.

3. Reread p. 9 and p. 15. Do you think there is a connection between the events on these pages? Explain your answer using details from the text.

Responses will vary but might include how both

pages have additional facts in the boxes.

Children analyze and respond to literary and informational text.

Name _____

DIRECTIONS Write a paragraph that summarizes why Madison and Rhiannon wanted to make a change and what change they made. Identify the text features that helped you write your paragraph. Use examples from the text to support your answer.

Responses should include that they wanted to save

the orangutans by getting companies to stop using

palm oil.

Conventions

Using Prepositions Circle the prepositional phrase in the sentence below. Then write your own sentences using prepositional phrases.

I. Our favorite activity is to walk fast (in the park.)

2. Sentences should include prepositional phrases

3. such as *on the door* or *under the cup.*

Children write routinely for a range of tasks, purposes, and audiences. Children practice various conventions of standard English.

Name _____

DIRECTIONS Write sentences using the words below.

homeless donated disaster

Responses should show contextual understanding of the words.

> **Write in Response to Reading**

DIRECTIONS Reread pp. 22–23 of *Change Makers*. Choose one photo. What part of the text does it help you understand? Use details from the text and photos to support your answer.

Responses should explain how the selected photo leads to a better understanding of the text.

Children demonstrate contextual understanding of Benchmark Vocabulary. Children read text closely and use text evidence in their written answers.

Name _____

DIRECTIONS Choose two illustrations in *Change Makers* and write the page number for each one. Then write several sentences that tell how the illustrations help you understand the text, the people, and the setting.

Page _____ : _Responses will vary but should have_

page numbers for two photos and details about how

the photos help in understanding the content. Example:

The photo on p.15 shows what orangutans look like.

Page _____ : _____

Children analyze and respond to literary and informational text.

Name _____

DIRECTIONS Reread the "Backpacks for Kids" section on p. 20 of *Change Makers*. Draw an illustration that shows Zach giving a backpack to a child. Then write a caption for your illustration.

Responses will vary but should include a drawing of Zach giving a backpack to a child.

The caption should tell about the picture.

Conventions

Using Conjunctions Write two of your own sentences that use conjunctions.

I. Sentences should have a conjunction, such

2. as *but, so,* or *and.*

Children write routinely for a range of tasks, purposes, and audiences. Children practice various conventions of standard English.

Name _____

DIRECTIONS Write sentences using the words below.

healthy harvest projects

Responses should show contextual understanding of

the words.

> Write in
> Response to
> Reading

DIRECTIONS Reread pp. 26–27 of *Change Makers*. What is community action? How do you know? Use examples from the text to support your answer.

Community action is when the community works

together. In the text, the communities work together

to garden and to paint murals.

Children demonstrate contextual
understanding of Benchmark Vocabulary.
Children read text closely and use text
evidence in their written answers.

Name _____

DIRECTIONS Revisit pp. 24–27 of *Change Makers.* Select a few pages and tell about how these pages help you understand the author's purpose. Use evidence from the text to support your ideas.

Responses will vary but should use evidence from the text that includes how kids working with adults can help make changes, either by planting community gardens or by painting murals.

Children analyze and respond to literary and informational text.

Name _____

DIRECTIONS Revise the paragraph you wrote in Lesson 2. Be sure to use conjunctions and prepositional phrases correctly. Revisit the text to help you.

Responses will vary, but paragraphs should be edited to include conjunctions and prepositional phrases.

Conventions

Using Conjunctions Write sentences to link the subjects below using the conjunctions *and, but,* and *or.*

1. The teacher, his students.

 Responses will vary but

2. sandwich, apple

 should include either *and,*

3. change, country

 but,* or *or.

Children write routinely for a range of tasks, purposes, and audiences. Children practice various conventions of standard English.

DIRECTIONS Write sentences using the words below.

champions links

Responses should show contextual understanding of the words.

Write in Response to Reading

DIRECTIONS Reread pp. 30–31 of *Change Makers.* How can someone turn an idea into action? Use details from the text to support your answer.

Responses should use evidence from the text, including Steps 1–4.

Children demonstrate contextual understanding of Benchmark Vocabulary. Children read text closely and use text evidence in their written answers.

Name _____

DIRECTIONS Using evidence from the text, answer the following questions about pp. 24–31 of *Change Makers*.

1. Revisit pp. 24–25. What reasons does the author provide to support the idea that adults need kids to take action?

They need hardworking kids who can plant and

water gardens.

2. Reread pp. 28–29. What reasons does the author provide to support the idea that it's important to get involved?

Making the world better takes people who can

help.

3. Reread pp. 30–31. Which step do you think is most important? Why?

Responses will vary, but opinions should tell

which step is most important and why.

Children analyze and respond to literary and informational text.

Writing

DIRECTIONS Write a paragraph that summarizes the way young people in *Change Makers* found ways to help their communities. You may use one of the topic sentences suggested in class, but you should include your own concluding sentence.

Responses will vary but should include some of

the ways described in the text and a concluding

sentence.

Conventions

Use Conjunctions Use each pair of verbs in a sentence. Link the verbs using the conjunction *and*.

I. shouted, cheered

Responses should include the conjunction *and.*

2. twirl, leap

Responses should include the conjunction *and.*

Children write routinely for a range of tasks, purposes, and audiences. Children practice various conventions of standard English.

Name _____

Long *o* Spelled *o*, *oa*, and *ow*

co*bra* b**oa**t b**ow**

Circle the word in each row with the long *o* sound.
Write the word on the line.

1. (toad) top two **toad**

2. bog book (bowl) **bowl**

3. took toss (toast) **toast**

4. out (over) one **over**

5. (most) moss mop **most**

6. spoon (show) shoe **show**

7. hot (hold) hook **hold**

8. play pot (photo) **photo**

9. (veto) vet vane **veto**

10. good got (grow) **grow**

Children apply grade-level phonics and word analysis skills.

DIRECTIONS Write sentences using the words below.

electronic solve

Responses should show contextual understanding of the words.

DIRECTIONS Revisit *Change Makers.* How do the illustrations help you identify the main topic? Use examples from the text to support your answer.

Responses will vary but might include that the illustrations explain or extend the text.

Children demonstrate contextual understanding of Benchmark Vocabulary. Children read text closely and use text evidence in their written answers.

Name _____

DIRECTIONS Choose a teacher, principal, or parent that you would like to interview and plan questions to ask them. Write down three questions that you would ask, but answer them as if you are the person being interviewed. Then write a paragraph, using your answers, that informs people about how that person helps the community.

Responses will vary, but paragraphs should include three ways a teacher, principal, or parent helps the community.

Conventions

Use Conjunctions Combine the phrases below with the conjunction *and* to make a complete sentence.

I. school was out for the summer

we made plans to go to the beach

School was out for the summer, and we made plans to go to the beach.

Children write routinely for a range of tasks, purposes, and audiences. Children practice various conventions of standard English.

Name _____

DIRECTIONS Write sentences using the words below.

heap rubble

Responses should show contextual understanding of the words.

DIRECTIONS Reread pp. 137–142 of *City Green.* Why do you think Old Man Hammer is as cranky as he is? Use details from the text to support your answer.

Responses will vary but might include that he thought the building should have been saved.

Children demonstrate contextual understanding of Benchmark Vocabulary. Children read text closely and use text evidence in their written answers.

Name _____

DIRECTIONS Using text evidence, answer the following questions about the beginning, middle, and end of *City Green.*

1. List three of your favorite events in chronological order.

<u>**Responses will vary but should include any**</u>

<u>**three events in order.**</u>

2. Reread the last paragraph on p. 148. Why does Marcy's mama tell her that she's making something happen? Use examples from the text to support your answer.

<u>**Mama sees the results of their work to clear**</u>

<u>**the lot.**</u>

3. Reread p. 162. How has Old Man Hammer changed? Use examples from the text to support your answer.

<u>**Responses will vary but should include that he**</u>

<u>**now thinks the lot is good.**</u>

Children analyze and respond to literary and informational text.

Writing

DIRECTIONS Think about how the new garden improved Marcy's neighborhood. Then write a paragraph that tells how people in your community might respond to having a neighborhood garden or park. Be sure to include details about how the people in your neighborhood would respond to the garden or park.

Responses will vary but should include details that tell how people would respond to the garden or park.

Conventions

Adjectives Circle the adjectives in the sentences below.

1. The (muddy) lot was soon changed into a (beautiful) garden.

2. When Old Man Hammer sees his (little) garden, his (sour) grapes turn (sweet.)

Children write routinely for a range of tasks, purposes, and audiences. Children practice various conventions of standard English.

DIRECTIONS Write sentences using the words below.

packets scoop

Responses should show contextual understanding of the words.

Write in Response to Reading

DIRECTIONS Reread pp. 140–141 of *City Green.* What does Old Man Hammer see that makes him sad? Use evidence from the text to support your answer.

He sees a trash-filled lot on a city block.

Children demonstrate contextual understanding of Benchmark Vocabulary. Children read text closely and use text evidence in their written answers.

Name _____

Josh Gibson, Home Run King

Josh Gibson's first love was baseball. In his spare time, Gibson could be found improving his skills and showing off his talent. One night in 1930, Gibson went to watch his hometown team, the Homestead Grays, play against the Kansas City Monarchs. That night changed everything.

The Grays' catcher was injured. The team's owner remembered seeing eighteen-year-old Gibson play ball. He invited the young athlete to play that night. The owner was so impressed that he asked Gibson to join the team. Gibson played professional baseball for the rest of his life.

Josh Gibson was a great player. He hit hundreds of home runs. Gibson led the Negro National League in home runs for ten years. He could hit a baseball harder and farther than almost any other player in the history of the game. He was a skilled catcher too. He earned a place in the Baseball Hall of Fame. But Josh Gibson didn't play in the Major Leagues. The Major Leagues were closed to African American players at the time. Three months after Gibson's death in 1947, Jackie Robinson became the first African American to play in the Major Leagues. He carried on Gibson's tradition of baseball excellence.

Children read text closely to determine what the text says.

Name _____

Look for Clues

Underline details in the text that prove that baseball was important to Josh Gibson.

Look for Clues: Extend Your Ideas

Write a clue that tells why Gibson probably would have wanted to play in the Major Leagues.

- -

Example: He was a great player.

Ask Questions

Write a question about baseball.

- -

Responses should include a baseball-related question.

Make Your Case

Circle the four facts that you feel were the most important.
Children should circle any four facts.

Make Your Case: Extend Your Ideas

Write a note to a friend that tells about an important fact you learned.

- -

Responses should include a fact from the text.

Children read text closely to determine what the text says.

Name _____

DIRECTIONS Write a letter to your city or town and tell them about an idea to improve the community. Use specific details to describe your improvement. Include a diagram or illustration to help your reader understand the plan.

Responses will vary but letters should include details

to describe an idea, in addition to a diagram or an

illustration to describe the idea.

Conventions

Formal and Informal Language Use formal or informal language to answer the questions below.

1. Write the start of a letter to a teacher.

Responses should include formal language.

2. Write the start of an e-mail to a friend.

Responses should include informal language.

Children write routinely for a range of tasks, purposes, and audiences. Children practice various conventions of standard English.

DIRECTIONS Write a sentence using the word below.

petition

Responses should show contextual understanding

of the word.

DIRECTIONS Reread pp. 144–145. Why does Old Man Hammer refuse to sign the petition? Use details from the text to support your answer.

Responses will vary but should include that he says,

"And nothin' is what's gonna happen."

Children demonstrate contextual understanding of Benchmark Vocabulary. Children read text closely and use text evidence in their written answers.

Unit 3 • Module B • Lesson 9 • 219

Name _____

DIRECTIONS Look at your Venn Diagram. Think about how Marcy and Old Man Hammer compare to each other as characters. Then write a paragraph that compares and contrasts the two characters' points of view. Remember to include information from your Venn Diagram. Use details from the text to support your answer.

Responses will vary but should use evidence from the text to point out that both characters are sad about the lot. However, Marcy takes action while Old Man Hammer does not.

Children analyze and respond to literary and informational text.

Name _____

DIRECTIONS Imagine that you are a visitor to Marcy's neighborhood. Write a paragraph that explains how Marcy's garden changed the neighborhood and why it is important to the community. Use examples from the text to support your answer.

Responses should use text evidence to explain how

the garden changes the neighborhood, such as by

bringing neighbors together.

Conventions

Formal and Informal Language Circle the sentence that is written using informal language. Then write why it is informal on the line below.

How are you today, madam?

Yo, how's it goin', dude?

The sentence includes slang and contractions.

Children write routinely for a range of tasks, purposes, and audiences. Children practice various conventions of standard English.

Name _____

DIRECTIONS Write sentences using the words below.

sprinkling patch

Responses should show contextual understanding of the words.

Write in Response to Reading

DIRECTIONS Reread pp. 162–163 of *City Green*. What does the illustration tell you about Old Man Hammer's character? Use details from the text to support your answer.

He is not afraid to change his mind because he says the lot is "nothin' but good."

Children demonstrate contextual understanding of Benchmark Vocabulary. Children read text closely and use text evidence in their written answers.

Name _____

DIRECTIONS Using text evidence, answer the following questions about pp. 156–165 of *City Green*.

1. Reread pp. 156–157. How do the illustrations help you understand what is happening?

 I see people working and Mr. Hammer going into

 the garden.

2. Reread pp. 160–161. How do the illustrations help you visualize the story?

 I can see the sections planted by different

 people.

3. Look through pp. 156–165. Write several sentences about an illustration that you would like to add to the story, or about an existing one that you would like to change. Use examples from the text to support your answer.

 Responses should include sentences about an

 illustration on one page.

Children analyze and respond to literary and informational text.

DIRECTIONS Design a small garden or park for your neighborhood. Think about the garden in *City Green* for ideas. Write the qualities and characteristics that your garden or park will have. Then tell how it will benefit your neighborhood and community. Remember to include two rules that all visitors must follow.

Responses should include a description of the

garden, how it benefits the community, and two rules

visitors must follow.

Conventions

Adjectives Write two sentences that describe you. Circle the adjectives that you use.

Responses should include two sentences about the

child, with the adjectives circled.

Children write routinely for a range of tasks, purposes, and audiences. Children practice various conventions of standard English.

Name _____

Compound Words

Say the word for each picture.
Use two words to make a compound word that names the picture.
Write the compound word on the line.

river + bank = riverbank

1.

spoon pot table tea

teapot

2.

coats drops rain shoes

raindrops

3.

air box mail plane

mailbox

4.

shoe tie lace neck

necklace

Find the word that you can put together with *meal* to make a compound word.
Mark the space to show your answer.

5. _____ meal
- ○ dinner
- ● oat
- ○ book

6. meal _____
- ● time
- ○ spoon
- ○ napkin

Children apply grade-level phonics and word analysis skills.

Name _____

DIRECTIONS Write a sentence using the word below.

undoubtedly

Responses should show contextual understanding of

the word.

Write in Response to Reading

DIRECTIONS Look at the structure of the poem "City Trees." Then look at the structure of the haikus in *Poems from Cricket Never Does.* Which kind of poem structure do you like better? Why?

Responses will vary but should include the preferred

structure and reasons why it is preferred.

Children demonstrate contextual understanding of Benchmark Vocabulary. Children read text closely and use text evidence in their written answers.

DIRECTIONS Revise your explanation from the previous lesson. Reread your writing, make notes about places you can revise, and then revise your explanation. Then write 1–2 sentences below that summarize how you made your writing stronger.

Responses will vary but the sentences should summarize the edits.

Formal and Informal Language Circle the formal English examples. Cross out the informal English examples.

~~Hello!~~ (Hello!)

~~Yo!~~

~~She ain't very happy.~~

~~I'm gonna go to the store.~~

(I am going to the store.)

(She is not very happy.)

 Children write routinely for a range of tasks, purposes, and audiences. Children practice various conventions of standard English.

Name _____

DIRECTIONS Write sentences using the words below.

healthy harvest petition

Responses should show
contextual understanding of the
words.

**Write in
Response to
Reading**

DIRECTIONS Think back over *Change Makers* and *City Green*. Do you think the people discussed in *Change Makers* worked as hard as the characters in *City Green*? Use text evidence to support your answer.

Responses should use evidence
from the text to support
opinions.

Children demonstrate contextual understanding of
Benchmark Vocabulary. Children read text closely and
use text evidence in their written answers.

Name _____

DIRECTIONS Reread pp. 24–27 of *Change Makers* and pp. 151–155 of *City Green.* Then write a paragraph that compares the language used in both texts. How is the language similar? How is it different? Use specific details from both texts to support your answer.

Responses will vary but should include that both texts are told in the third-person. *Change Makers,* unlike *City Green,* uses formal language, includes a Fact File, and does not include dialogue.

Children analyze and respond to literary and informational text.

DIRECTIONS Reread pp. 24–27 of *Change Makers* and pp. 151–155 of *City Green.* Look at the illustrations and note the hard work that people are doing. Write a paragraph that compares how each selection describes hard work. What descriptive words and phrases do the authors use? Use details from both texts to support your answer.

Responses will vary but may include "hardworking"

and "needs kids to help" from *Change Makers;* and

"workers took the rubble away," "I am digging away,"

and "all day long he piles junk" from *City Green.*

Conventions

Formal and Informal Language Rewrite the sentences below, changing the informal English to formal English.

I can't wait to go on our trip. We're gonna go hiking, dude! The mountain peak is like way up there. Wanna come with?

I cannot wait to go on our trip. We are going to go hiking!

The mountain peak is high. Do you want to come?

Children write routinely for a range of tasks, purposes, and audiences. Children practice various conventions of standard English.

Name _____

Compound Words

Say the word for each picture.
Use two words to make a compound word.
Write the compound word on the line.

1.

bow coat rain storm

rainbow

2.

bath bird dog house

birdhouse

3.

brush hair pick tooth

toothbrush

4.

ball base foot print

football

Read the story. **Circle** the compound words.

Reiko was doing her homework by the fireplace. Her eyesight was bad, so she had her eyeglasses on. She heard a footstep outside the window. She picked up her flashlight and went outside to look. Someone had left footprints in the backyard. Reiko went inside. She would have been able to see the footprints better in daylight. Then she saw a man in the moonlight. It was her dad. He had made the footprints. Everything was okay.

Children apply grade-level phonics and word analysis skills.

Lesson 1

Name _____

Benchmark Vocabulary

DIRECTIONS Write a sentence using the word below.

dialect

Responses should show contextual understanding of

the word.

Write in
Response to
Reading

DIRECTIONS Reread pp. 1–16 of *The Earth Dragon Awakes.* What points of view do the boys have about their fathers? Use examples from the text to support your answer.

Henry doesn't want to be like his father because all

he does is add numbers in the bank; Chin thinks his

father is kind and works hard but is not a hero.

Children demonstrate contextual understanding of Benchmark Vocabulary. Children read text closely and use text evidence in their written answers.

Name _____

DIRECTIONS Flag details that reveal Henry's and Chin's points of view about their parents. Then write a scene between Henry and Chin that reveals their points of view. Use thoughts, feelings, and actions to show the point of view of each character.

Responses should include that neither boy thought

his father was interesting. The scene reveals the

points of view through the boys' words, feelings, and

actions.

Conventions

Common and Proper Nouns Circle the common nouns. Cross out the proper nouns. Then write two of your own sentences using common and proper nouns.

1. (earthquake) ~~San Francisco~~ (fire)
 (umbrella) ~~Henry~~ ~~Chin~~

2. Sentences should include at least one common

3. noun or one proper noun.

 Children write routinely for a range of tasks, purposes, and audiences. Children practice various conventions of standard English.

Name _____

DIRECTIONS Write sentences using the words below.

twitches plunges dazed

Responses should show contextual understanding of

the words.

Write in Response to Reading

DIRECTIONS Reread pp. 17–39 of *The Earth Dragon Awakes.* How does Chin feel when he's buried in the rubble? Use evidence from the text to support your answer.

Responses should use evidence from the text

including that Chin feels as if he cannot even

breathe.

Children demonstrate contextual understanding of Benchmark Vocabulary. Children read text closely and use text evidence in their written answers.

Name _____

DIRECTIONS Using evidence from the text, answer the following question about pp. 36–39 of *The Earth Dragon Awakes.* Write a few sentences about how the characters in this section respond to the earthquake. What words does the author use to show you how the characters feel?

Responses will vary but should include text evidence from pp. 36–39 of *The Earth Dragon Awakes* including that the scared neighbors are acting like heroes, but the driver is not.

Children analyze and respond to literary and informational text.

Name _____

DIRECTIONS Choose a character in the lesson to write about. Then write a paragraph that describes how that character faced the challenges he or she was confronted with during the earthquake.

Responses should include the challenges one character

faces. Example: Mr. Travis organizes the neighbors to

rescue people from the rubble and put out the fire.

Capitalize Proper Nouns Capitalize the proper nouns in the sentences below. Then write the corrected sentences on the lines.

1. The cable car arrives, and henry climbs on.

The cable car arrives, and Henry climbs on.

2. But fear twists inside chin like a snake.

But fear twists inside Chin like a snake.

Children write routinely for a range of tasks, purposes, and audiences. Children practice various conventions of standard English.

DIRECTIONS Write sentences using the words below.

scatters missiles

Responses should show contextual understanding of

the words.

Write in
Response to
Reading

DIRECTIONS Reread pp. 44–46 of *The Earth Dragon Awakes*. What does Ah Sing do that changes his son's mind about him? Use examples from the text to support your answer.

Responses should include that Ah Sing stands in

front of the charging bull to save his son. Now Chin

knows he was wrong to think his father was dull.

Children demonstrate contextual understanding of Benchmark Vocabulary. Children read text closely and use text evidence in their written answers.

Name _____

A Real-Life Action Hero

Eric listened closely to the first-aid lesson at his Cub Scout meeting. The guest speaker was talking about the Heimlich maneuver. This action can help someone who is choking. It causes whatever is caught in the choking person's throat to come out. (Later) Eric saw a television program that taught him more about it. He practiced with his mother. He followed the Cub Scout motto "Be prepared." He had no idea how important that lesson would be.

(One day) Eric's little sister Jessie was having a snack. Their mother heard Jessie choking. Jessie could not breathe. Nothing their mother did helped.

She called for Eric's help. (Then) she rushed to call 9-1-1. But Eric was ready. (Before) his mother could tell the 9-1-1 operator what was happening, Eric sprang into action.

He wrapped his arms around Jessie from behind. He did exactly what he had practiced with his mother. The egg Jessie had been eating popped right out! Jessie was safely breathing again. Ten-year-old Eric was a hero.

Children read text closely to determine what the text says.

Name _____

Look for Clues

Tell why the order of events is important in this story.

It helps the reader understand the action.

Look for Clues: Extend Your Ideas

Circle words or phrases in the story that help you to follow the order of events.

Ask Questions

Write a question that you have about a home emergency.

Responses should be about an emergency.

Ask Questions: Extend Your Ideas

Write a question that you would ask Eric about learning such an important safety skill.

Responses should fit the story context.

Make Your Case

Tell a friend whether you think the fictional characters make this story more interesting.

Responses should be supported by reasons.

Make Your Case: Extend Your Ideas

Underline a sentence that you found to be most interesting.

Children read text closely to determine what the text says.

Name _____

DIRECTIONS Choose a scene from *The Earth Dragon Awakes.* Then rewrite the scene from Henry's or Chin's point of view. Remember to include dialogue to show their thoughts, feelings, and actions.

Responses will vary but should be told from Henry's

or Chin's point of view. Dialogue should suggest

thoughts, feelings, and actions.

Conventions

Identify Singular and Plural Nouns Circle the singular nouns. Cross out the plural nouns. Then write your own sentence that uses a singular or plural noun.

1. ~~books~~ (ladder) (wagon) ~~bricks~~ ~~pails~~ ~~houses~~

2. ~~carts~~ (door) ~~horses~~ ~~rivers~~ ~~nails~~ (rock)

3. Sentence should have a singular or plural noun.

Children write routinely for a range of tasks, purposes, and audiences. Children practice various conventions of standard English.

Name _____

DIRECTIONS Write sentences using the words below.

surges trample

<u>Responses should show contextual understanding of</u>

<u>the words.</u>

> **Write in Response to Reading**

DIRECTIONS Revisit pp. 62–81 of *The Earth Dragon Awakes*. Choose a character from this section whom you think is a hero. What is it about that character's response to events that makes him or her a hero? Use evidence from the text to support your answer.

<u>Responses should include support from the text to</u>

<u>explain how the chosen character acted like a hero.</u>

Children demonstrate contextual understanding of Benchmark Vocabulary. Children read text closely and use text evidence in their written answers.

Name _____

DIRECTIONS Revisit pp. 62–81 of *The Earth Dragon Awakes.* Choose two characters from this section and write a paragraph that compares and contrasts each character's response to the earthquake. Use evidence from the text to support your answer.

Responses will vary but should use text evidence to support the response. Example: Ah Sing is crippled, but still tries to help load the materials; Ah Quon is big and powerful, with a broad back, and he too loads the wagon.

Children analyze and respond to literary and informational text.

Name _____

DIRECTIONS Choose one character and one event from pp. 62–81 of *The Earth Dragon Awakes.* Then write a narrative paragraph about the actions that character took in response to the event. Use evidence from the text to support your answer.

Responses will vary but should include a narrative

about the actions that a character took in response

to an event.

Conventions

Identify Irregular Plural Nouns Write two of your own sentences that use irregular plural nouns.

1. Responses will vary but sentences should

include irregular plural nouns. Examples: *men,*

2. *women,* and *children*

Children write routinely for a range of tasks, purposes, and audiences.
Children practice various conventions of standard English.

DIRECTIONS Write sentences using the words below.

revenge parched

Responses should show contextual understanding of

the words.

DIRECTIONS Reread pp. 102–105 of *The Earth Dragon Awakes.* What happens at the end of the story? Use key details from the text to support your answer.

Responses should use text evidence including the

boys leave the book because heroes are right under

their noses.

Children demonstrate contextual understanding of Benchmark Vocabulary. Children read text closely and use text evidence in their written answers.

DIRECTIONS Using evidence from the text, answer the following questions about pp. 82–105 of *The Earth Dragon Awakes.*

1. Reread pp. 89–92. Write several sentences about the Great Fire. What events happened that made this fire so large and terrible? Use evidence from the text to support your answer.

<u>Responses will vary but should include the events</u>

<u>that made the fire so large and terrible.</u>

2. Reread pp. 96–99. Summarize the events that take place in this section. What do the people of San Francisco do to control the fire? Use specific details from the text to support your answer.

<u>Responses should include details such as the</u>

<u>firemen build a firebreak, but the Great Fire</u>

<u>continues; the men will not give up.</u>

Children analyze and respond to literary and informational text.

DIRECTIONS Choose a scene from *The Earth Dragon Awakes* to expand upon. Use temporal words to tell the sequence of the events. Remember to wrap up your scene with a conclusion.

Responses will vary but should include an expanded

scene that includes temporal words and ends with a

concluding statement.

Conventions

Identify Collective Nouns Circle the collective nouns. Then write your own sentence about *The Earth Dragon Awakes* that uses a collective noun.

1. person (family) (team) student (crew)

2. The sentence should include a collective noun.

Children write routinely for a range of tasks, purposes, and audiences. Children practice various conventions of standard English.

Name _____

Long *i* Spelled *i, ie, igh, y*

ch**i**ld

n**igh**t

cr**y**

t**ie**

Circle a word to finish each sentence.

1. Things seem darker after you look at something _____ _____.

bite bring (bright)

2. You can _____ out for yourself.

fin (find) fight

3. Put some gray paper _____ some black paper.

bit (by) bite

4. Put it _____ next to white paper.

rid (right) rye

Read the first word. **Circle** the word in each row with the same vowel sound as the first word.

5. spider: (tiger) trigger ticket

6. pie: undo unlock (untie)

7. light: finger finish (fright)

8. fly: (shy) ship shin

Children apply grade-level phonics and word analysis skills.

Name _____

DIRECTIONS Write sentences using the words below.

insurance ruins

Responses should show contextual understanding of the word.

Write in Response to Reading

DIRECTIONS Reread pp. 107–117 of *The Earth Dragon Awakes.* Write several sentences about two connections that you made between the story and the facts in the Afterword. Use evidence from the text to explain the connections.

Responses will vary but may include that many buildings were destroyed and many people died, but the city was rebuilt.

 Children demonstrate contextual understanding of Benchmark Vocabulary. Children read text closely and use text evidence in their written answers.

Name _____

DIRECTIONS Write a sequence of events from Henry's or Chin's life that is connected to a historical or scientific event. Use temporal words to signal the order of events. Remember to revisit the Afterword to find historical and scientific facts about the earthquake.

Responses should use temporal words to describe a

sequence of events from a character's life. Responses

should be connected to an event in the Afterword.

Past and Present Verb Tense Change each present tense verb to past tense. Then write your own present and past tense verbs.

1. skates _skated_

2. bakes _baked_

3. _Responses should include present tense verbs and_

4. _the past tense of those verbs._

 Children write routinely for a range of tasks, purposes, and audiences. Children practice various conventions of standard English.

Name _____

DIRECTIONS Write sentences using the words below.

confidence courage

Responses should show contextual understanding of

the words.

Write in
Response to
Reading

DIRECTIONS Reread pp. 102–105 of *The Earth Dragon Awakes*. How does the ending of the book relate to the author's central message? Use evidence from the text to support your answer.

Responses might include that people aren't always

as they appear. For example, both boys changed their

opinions of their fathers.

Children demonstrate contextual understanding of Benchmark Vocabulary. Children read text closely and use text evidence in their written answers.

Name _____

DIRECTIONS Using evidence from the text, answer the following questions about *The Earth Dragon Awakes.*

1. What is a central message?

Responses will vary but should include something about the lessons that the characters learn.

2. Think back to the events of *The Earth Dragon Awakes.* Choose three events from the text and explain how they contribute to the central message. Use specific details and evidence to support your answer.

Responses will vary but should include references to heroes and evidence from the text.

Children analyze and respond to literary and informational text.

Name _____

DIRECTIONS On a separate sheet of paper, write a scene from either Henry's or Chin's point of view that tells the central message of the story. Include details about how the character feels and what he is thinking. Describe the character's actions. Revisit *The Earth Dragon Awakes* to look for examples of how the author shows what a character is feeling and thinking.

Responses should include details about how the selected character feels and what he thinks.

Conventions

Nouns and Verbs Underline the nouns. Circle the verbs. Then write your own sentence. Remember to underline the noun and circle the verb.

1. The fire spread quickly.

2. The dog howled loudly.

3. The Great Earthquake and Fire destroyed more than 28,000 houses, stores, and other buildings.

4. Responses should include an underlined noun

and a circled verb.

Children write routinely for a range of tasks, purposes, and audiences. Children practice various conventions of standard English.

Name _____

DIRECTIONS Write sentences using the words below.

fortune advised

Responses should show contextual understanding of

the words.

Write in Response to Reading

DIRECTIONS Reread pp. 5–11 of *Seek the Sun.* Whose point of view do you most agree with—the sandalmaker or the builder? Use evidence from the text to support your answer.

Responses will vary but should use evidence from

the text to support the response. Example: Offices are

needed, and the builder says he has no place on the

ground to build. I agree with him.

Children demonstrate contextual understanding of Benchmark Vocabulary. Children read text closely and use text evidence in their written answers.

Name _____

DIRECTIONS Think about the points of view of the builder and the people affected by the building's shadow. On a separate sheet of paper, write a story scene that expresses the builder's or the neighbor's point of view. Revisit pp. 7–8 of *Seek the Sun* to find evidence of thoughts, feelings, and actions that reveal the character's point of view. Then, use this evidence to help reveal the character's point of view in your scene.

Scenes should use text evidence to support the character's point of view.

Conventions

Irregular Verbs Write the underlined present tense verb as a past tense verb.

1. I <u>eat</u> cereal for breakfast.

ate _____

2. She <u>builds</u> a fence around the building.

built _____

3. They <u>find</u> a crowd of angry people.

found _____

Children write routinely for a range of tasks, purposes, and audiences. Children practice various conventions of standard English.

Name _____

DIRECTIONS Write sentences using the words below.

tended lovingly precious

Responses should show contextual understanding of

the words.

Write in
Response to
Reading

DIRECTIONS Reread pp. 5–8 of *Seek the Sun*. Do you think it would have been understandable if the sandalmaker's wife had gotten just as upset as her husband? Use evidence from the text to support your answer.

Responses should use evidence from the text to

support the opinion. Example: Yes. The wife lives

under the same conditions.

Children demonstrate contextual understanding of Benchmark Vocabulary. Children read text closely and use text evidence in their written answers.

Name _____

DIRECTIONS Reread pp. 7–8 of *Seek the Sun.* Find details in this section that tell how both the sandalmaker **and** his wife responded to the tall building. Then write these details on the lines below.

Responses will vary but should include that the man is upset, saying they can't wrestle a dragon. However, the wife remains calm and comes up with a plan to go to court.

Children analyze and respond to literary and informational text.

Name _____

DIRECTIONS Consider the responses of the sandalmaker and his wife in the story. Flag text evidence that reveals how each character responded to a challenge. On a separate sheet of paper, describe how each character responded to the challenge they faced. Use thoughts, feelings, and actions to reveal and describe how they responded.

Responses will vary but might include that the man is upset, but the wife makes a plan.

Conventions

Irregular Verbs Read the present tense verbs. Cross out the incorrect past tense verbs. Then write two of your own sentences using irregular past tense verbs.

1.

Present Tense	Past Tense	Past Tense
swim	swam	~~swimmed~~
keep	~~keeped~~	kept

2. **Responses will vary, but both sentences should**

include irregular past tense verbs, such as *went*,

3. ***grew*, and *said*.**

Children write routinely for a range of tasks, purposes, and audiences. Children practice various conventions of standard English.

DIRECTIONS Write sentences using the words below.

essential protected

Responses should show contextual understanding of

the words.

DIRECTIONS Reread pp. 8–11 of *Seek the Sun*. Do you think knowing that the story is based on a real court case makes it better? Explain why or why not.

Responses will vary but opinions should be

supported with reasons. Example: Yes, I like that the

story is based on some facts. I think that makes it

more interesting.

Children demonstrate contextual understanding of Benchmark Vocabulary. Children read text closely and use text evidence in their written answers.

Name _____

DIRECTIONS Write a description of the park at the end of *Seek the Sun*. Tell how the author's description of the park helps to provide closure for the reader. Use evidence from the text to support your answer.

Responses will vary. Descriptions should use text evidence including a pond, trees, benches, and stone paths. The description provides closure because their fortune that "light will fill an empty space" becomes true.

Children analyze and respond to literary and informational text.

Lesson 10

Name _____

Writing

DIRECTIONS Choose six events from the story and flag text evidence that describes each event. On a separate sheet of paper, write a sentence that describes each event. Remember that your description of each event must include evidence from the text. Then, use these descriptions to create a storyboard. Make your pictures as detailed as possible to support your sentences.

Responses should include a storyboard consisting of any six scenes, based on text evidence, shown in sequential order.

Conventions

Irregular Verbs Write the past tense verb for each present tense verb.

1. see _saw_

2. come _came_

3. sing _sang_

4. catch _caught_

260 • Unit 4 • Module A • Lesson 10

Children write routinely for a range of tasks, purposes, and audiences. Children practice various conventions of standard English.

Copyright © Pearson Education, Inc., or its affiliates. All Rights Reserved.

Name _____

Comparative Endings -er, -est

Circle a word to finish each sentence.
Write the word on the line.

Spot is **big**.
Rover is **bigger**.
Spike is **biggest**.

smaller (smallest)

1. The spotted one is the

smallest .

(taller) tallest

2. Nate is **taller** than Jack.

(happier) happiest

3. Ben is **happier** than Josh.

wetter (wettest)

4. Jill is the **wettest** of all.

(fatter) fattest

5. This clown is **fatter** than
that one.

Children apply grade-level phonics and word
analysis skills.

DIRECTIONS Write sentences using the words below.

shiver vanish tremble faint

Responses should show contextual understanding of

the words.

Write in Response to Reading

DIRECTIONS Reread "The Fool on the Hill" and "Mother of the Mountains." Why do you think cultures told myths about the same subject, such as thunder? Use evidence from both texts to support your answer.

Responses will vary. Example: People made up myths

to try to explain events in nature.

Children demonstrate contextual understanding of Benchmark Vocabulary. Children read text closely and use text evidence in their written answers.

Name _____

DIRECTIONS Think of another version of a myth about what causes thunder. On a separate sheet of paper, list the ideas, thoughts, feelings, and actions that your characters might engage in. Then write a first draft of your myth.

Responses will vary but should include a draft of an

original myth about thunder.

Conventions

Identify and Use Subject Pronouns Write your own sentences that use subject pronouns.

1. Sentences should include subject pronouns

2. such as *they, he, she,* or *it.*

Children write routinely for a range of tasks, purposes, and audiences. Children practice various conventions of standard English.

DIRECTIONS Write sentences using the words below.

dialect precious

Responses should show contextual understanding of

the words.

Write in
Response to
Reading

DIRECTIONS Revisit pp. 12–15 of *The Earth Dragon Awakes* and pp. 5–7 of *Seek the Sun*. What is similar about the dragon imagery in these stories? What is different? Use evidence from both texts to support your answers.

Responses should use text evidence, such as

each dragon is to be feared, but one is blamed for

earthquakes and the other for fierce winds.

Children demonstrate contextual understanding of Benchmark Vocabulary. Children read text closely and use text evidence in their written answers.

Name _____

DIRECTIONS Think about how people from different cultures may speak different languages and have different customs, habits, foods, and jobs. List ways the characters in *The Earth Dragon Awakes* and *Seek the Sun* are both alike and different. Use evidence from both texts to help you create your lists.

Responses will vary but might include the characters' reactions to problems in both texts; some characters help solve problems while others just complain.

Children analyze and respond to literary and informational text.

Name _____

DIRECTIONS Determine how you want your myth about what causes thunder to end. Craft a conclusion to your myth about what causes thunder. Then revise and edit your conclusion to address only the key details that are significant.

Children should revise their first draft to craft a

conclusion that includes key details.

Conventions

Object Pronouns Use an object pronoun to complete the sentences below. Then write your own sentence using an object pronoun.

1. Students went to the library. Their parents went with _____ them _____.

2. My brother is making a mess. Mom asked _____ him _____ to clean it up.

3. Sentence should include an object pronoun.

Children write routinely for a range of tasks, purposes, and audiences. Children practice various conventions of standard English.

DIRECTIONS Write sentences using the words below.

surges essential

Responses should show contextual understanding of

the words.

**Write in
Response to
Reading**

DIRECTIONS Write several sentences about the importance of the author's notes at the end of both *The Earth Dragon Awakes* and *Seek the Sun*. Use evidence from both texts to support your answer.

Responses should use text evidence including how

the notes point out that both stories are based on

fact. Reponses might state which events actually

happened.

Children demonstrate contextual understanding of Benchmark Vocabulary. Children read text closely and use text evidence in their written answers.

The Blank Book

Elias's dad was in the army. He was leaving home to be stationed in another country. As he said good-bye, Dad gave Elias a book. "I want you to read this when you get home," Dad said.

* Elias didn't feel like reading, but he opened the book anyway...and what a surprise! Every page was blank except the first one. There, Dad explained that they would take turns writing in the book, mailing it back and forth while Dad was gone.

Elias began writing immediately, telling his dad how much he missed him, and then he mailed the book. Three weeks later, the book came back. Dad wrote about a market he had visited. He described the sharp, spicy smells and bright, patterned carpets. He described the warm, buttery bread he tried.

Elias and his dad wrote often. Dad described what life was like on the base. Sometimes he invented silly stories or drew neat pictures. Elias wrote about home and school. He drew colorful pictures. They had to get another book before long, and then another!

When Dad came home, he had a new book with him. "I thought we could keep going," Dad said, grinning. Elias nodded. This was definitely a tradition he wanted to keep.

Children read text closely to determine what the text says.

Name _____

Look for Clues

Underline clues that show similarities between what Dad and Elias wrote. Circle clues that show differences between what they wrote.

Look for Clues: Extend Your Ideas

Star the sentence that tells how Elias felt when his dad first gave the book to him.

Ask Questions

Write a question you might ask Dad about where he is living.

Responses should be based on story context.

Ask Questions: Extend Your Ideas

Write a question Dad might ask Elias about school.

Responses should be based on story context.

Make Your Case

On a separate sheet of paper, write two things that could be actual events in the story. Tell why you believe they could be actual events.

Responses should be based on actual events.

Make Your Case: Extend Your Ideas

Highlight descriptive words the author uses to add to the fictional story.

 Children read text closely to determine what the text says.

DIRECTIONS Reread your revised draft several times. Check the spelling of any words that your partner circled. Then use the editing checklist compiled by your classmates to edit your revised draft.
Children use the editing checklist to edit their drafts.

Conventions

Identify Reflexive Pronouns Use a reflexive pronoun to complete the sentences below. Then write your own sentence that uses a reflexive pronoun.

1. As I prepared for my spelling test, I told

 myself

 to remain calm.

2. Because he was early for the movie, he had time to get

 himself

 set up with popcorn.

3. The sentence should use a reflexive pronoun

 such as *themselves.*

Children write routinely for a range of tasks, purposes, and audiences. Children practice various conventions of standard English.

Name _____

Final Syllable *-le*

ankle	bubble	bugle	people	table	turtle

Say the word for each picture.
Write the word on the line.
Use the words in the box if you need help.

 app**le**

1.	2.	3.
table	people	bubble

4.	5	6.
turtle	ankle	bugle

Circle the word in each sentence that ends with the same sound as *apple*.

7. José took a (tumble) when he tripped on the branch.

8. I got a new (puzzle) for my birthday.

9. Can you read the (title) of this book?

Children apply grade-level phonics and word analysis skills.

DIRECTIONS Write sentences using the words below.

rotating violent alerts

Responses should show contextual understanding of the words.

Write in Response to Reading

DIRECTIONS Reread the first paragraph on p. 5 of *Disaster Alert!* What is the focus of this paragraph? Use examples from the text to support your answer.

The focus is that tornadoes are dangerous because they move very fast. Average ground speed is 30 miles per hour; winds inside can reach 200 miles per hour.

Children demonstrate contextual understanding of Benchmark Vocabulary. Children read text closely and use text evidence in their written answers.

DIRECTIONS Choose a topic about tornadoes from pp. 4–9 of *Disaster Alert!* Write an informative paragraph that introduces the tornado-related topic and supports it with details. Use examples from the text to support your answer.

<u>Responses will vary but the informative paragraph</u>

<u>should introduce a topic described on pages 4–9 and</u>

<u>include examples from the text.</u>

Conventions

Use Adjectives Underline the adjectives in the sentences below.

1. It was a <u>cool</u>, <u>rainy</u> day.

2. The sky was <u>dark</u>.

3. The vegetable was <u>smelly</u> and <u>green</u>.

Children write routinely for a range of tasks, purposes, and audiences. Children practice various conventions of standard English.

Name _____

DIRECTIONS Write sentences using the words below.

absorb electrical

Responses should show contextual understanding of

the words.

Write in Response to Reading

DIRECTIONS Reread p. 11 of *Disaster Alert!* What happened in Tewkesbury, Gloucestershire, England in 2007? Use examples from the text to support your answer.

Responses will vary but should include text evidence

including that heavy rains fell. Two months' worth of

rain fell in one day.

Children demonstrate contextual understanding of Benchmark Vocabulary. Children read text closely and use text evidence in their written answers.

DIRECTIONS Reread pp. 12–13 of *Disaster Alert!* Write a few sentences that tell about the main topic of this section. Use evidence from the text to help you identify what the main topic is.

Responses should indicate that the main topic is floods. Children should describe some effects of a flood and how to survive a flood.

Children analyze and respond to literary and informational text.

Name _____

DIRECTIONS Review the paragraph you wrote in Lesson 1. Look for any terms that might require a definition. Use the sources provided to look up any definitions and to search for more details that might add to readers' understanding of your paragraph. Then add this information into your paragraph.

Children should review their paragraphs and provide more details that might add to readers' understanding.

Conventions

Use Adjectives Write two of your own sentences that use adjectives on the lines below.

1. Responses will vary but should

2. include adjectives.

Children write routinely for a range of tasks, purposes, and audiences. Children practice various conventions of standard English.

Name _____

DIRECTIONS Write sentences using the words below.

dissolves collapse explore

Responses should show contextual understanding of

the words.

Copyright © Pearson Education, Inc., or its affiliates. All Rights Reserved.

Write in Response to Reading

DIRECTIONS Reread pp. 18–19 of *Disaster Alert!* What reasons support the author's point that some sinkholes collapse quickly and without warning? Use examples from the text to support your answer.

Responses should cite evidence from the text

including the description of the sinkhole in Clermont,

Florida.

Children demonstrate contextual understanding of Benchmark Vocabulary. Children read text closely and use text evidence in their written answers.

DIRECTIONS Choose a topic from the list of natural disasters provided by your teacher, or from an idea of your own. Research facts and definitions related to your chosen natural disaster. Then write an informative/explanatory paragraph about your topic using facts and definitions from your research.

Responses will vary. The informative/explanatory

paragraph should be about a natural disaster and

include facts and definitions.

Conventions

Use Adjectives Circle the adjective. Tell which word the adjective describes.

1. The (rocky) plates below the ground move slowly.

plates

2. This creates a (violent) storm called a supercell.

storm

Children write routinely for a range of tasks, purposes, and audiences. Children practice various conventions of standard English.

Name _____

DIRECTIONS Write sentences using the words below.

pressure erupts poisons

Responses should show contextual understanding of

the words.

DIRECTIONS Reread p. 27 of *Disaster Alert!* What does the word *dormant* mean? How does knowing the meaning of the word help you learn about volcanoes? Use details from the text to support your answer.

Responses should use evidence from the text

including that *dormant* means volcanoes are not

erupting; volcanoes don't always erupt.

Children demonstrate contextual understanding of Benchmark Vocabulary. Children read text closely and use text evidence in their written answers.

DIRECTIONS Using evidence from the text, answer the following questions about pp. 22–27 of *Disaster Alert!*

1. Reread pp. 22–23. What escapes to the Earth's surface when a volcano erupts?

 magma_____

2. Where is the tallest volcano in the solar system located?

 Mars

3. Reread pp. 24–25. What should you do if a volcano erupts near you?

 One should act quickly.

4. Reread pp. 26–27. What does a volcanologist do?

 A volcanologist studies volcanoes.

5. Reread pp. 26–27. What does it mean to say that a volcano is *extinct?*

 It means the volcano is not likely to erupt.

Children analyze and respond to literary and informational text.

Name _____

DIRECTIONS Write a descriptive paragraph about a change caused by a natural event. Your paragraph should include at least two challenges this change caused for people. Introduce your topic, list at least two challenges, and write a concluding statement. Use descriptive words so your reader will be able to picture the change and the challenges it caused.

Responses will vary. Paragraphs should use

descriptive words to describe two challenges from a

change caused by a natural event.

Conventions

Adjectives Write two of your own sentences about a natural disaster. Circle the adjectives. Use information from pp. 22–27 of *Disaster Alert!* to help you.

1. Responses should use adjectives to describe a

2. natural disaster. Adjectives should be circled.

 Children write routinely for a range of tasks, purposes, and audiences. Children practice various conventions of standard English.

Benchmark Vocabulary

DIRECTIONS Write sentences using the words below.

faulty extreme shelters

Responses should show contextual understanding of the words.

Write in Response to Reading

DIRECTIONS Reread pp. 28–29 of *Disaster Alert!* What is a bushfire? Use details from the text to support your answer.

Responses should cite text evidence such as bushfires are fires that start in hot, dry places.

Children demonstrate contextual understanding of Benchmark Vocabulary. Children read text closely and use text evidence in their written answers.

Name _____

DIRECTIONS Using evidence from the text, answer the following questions about pp. 28–31 of *Disaster Alert!*

I. Why is it important to describe connections between scientific ideas in a text?

Responses will vary but might include something about identifying the main idea and gaining a deeper understanding.

2. Reread pp. 28–30. Write a few sentences about why you think bushfires caused so much destruction in Australia. Use evidence from the text to support your answer.

Responses will vary but should include the fact they are common in Australia, move quickly, and burn at very high temperatures.

Children analyze and respond to literary and informational text.

DIRECTIONS Revisit *Disaster Alert!* and collect key details from the text, illustrations, and diagrams. On a separate sheet of paper, organize your main ideas and details by creating a Main Idea and Details chart. Choose a central idea. Add your key ideas and details to your chart. Then write a summary based on the information in your chart.

Responses will vary but should include a summary of

the key ideas used in a Main Idea and Details chart.

Conventions

Adjectives Circle the adjectives. Then write your own sentence that includes two different adjectives.

1. The ground shook. I crawled under the (wooden) table for protection. My sister let out a (loud) screech. My (calming) words helped her. Earthquakes are (scary)!

2. **The sentence should use two adjectives.**

Children write routinely for a range of tasks, purposes, and audiences. Children practice various conventions of standard English.

Name _____

Vowel Patterns *oo, u*

c**oo**k	b**u**ll

full hood hook pull shook stood took wood

Write three words from the box that rhyme with **good**.

1. hood	2. wood	3. stood

Write three words from the box that rhyme with **look.**

4. hook	5. took	6. shook

Write a word from the box that is the opposite of each word below.

7. push	8. empty
pull	full

Write a word from the box to finish each sentence.

brook put

9. I _____put_____ a hook on the fishing pole.

10. I pulled a fish from the _____brook_____.

 Children apply grade-level phonics and word analysis skills.

Name _____

DIRECTIONS Write sentences using the words below.

damage wreck

Responses should show contextual understanding of

the words.

Write in
Response to
Reading

DIRECTIONS Revisit pp. 12–43 of *Danger! Earthquakes.* How does the title of the text help you identify the main topic? Use evidence from the text to support your answer.

Responses should use evidence from the text

including that the text is about the danger of

earthquakes.

Children demonstrate contextual understanding of Benchmark Vocabulary. Children read text closely and use text evidence in their written answers.

Name _____

DIRECTIONS Choose two earthquakes from *Danger! Earthquakes* to compare. Then write an informative/explanatory paragraph that uses key ideas and details from the text to help you compare them. Introduce your topic and develop your main points using key ideas and facts. Remember to provide a concluding statement.

Responses will vary but should include an

informative/explanatory paragraph that compares

two earthquakes, using key ideas and facts from

the text.

Conventions

Adverbs Underline the adverb in the sentence below. Then write your own sentence about earthquakes that uses an adverb.

1. I finished my homework <u>easily</u>.

2. The sentence should use an adverb.

Children write routinely for a range of tasks, purposes, and audiences. Children practice various conventions of standard English.

Name _____

DIRECTIONS Write sentences using the words below.

measure level recorded

Responses should show contextual understanding of

the words.

Write in
Response to
Reading

DIRECTIONS Reread pp. 14–15 of *Danger! Earthquakes.*
Do the images on these pages help you understand the
text? Use evidence from the text to support your answer.

Responses should use evidence from the images

and the text including that earthquakes knock down

buildings and wreck highways.

Children demonstrate contextual understanding of
Benchmark Vocabulary. Children read text closely and
use text evidence in their written answers.

DIRECTIONS Write several sentences that tell how the map on pp. 22–23 helps you to understand the text better.

Responses will vary. The map shows the places where most major earthquakes happen, including the Pacific Ring of Fire.

Children analyze and respond to literary and informational text.

Name _____

DIRECTIONS Revisit the map on pp. 22–23 of *Danger! Earthquakes*. Write two questions you have that can be answered by the map. Then answer those questions on the lines below using facts and definitions.

Responses will vary but should include two questions

that can be answered by the map. Example: Where

do most earthquakes happen? (Pacific Ring of Fire)

Why do you think the area is called Pacific Ring of

Fire? (The map shows a circle, or ring.)

Conventions

Adverbs Add an adverb to describe the verb. Examples are shown below.

1. The earthquake shook San Francisco _____violently_____.

2. Ports were _____completely_____ destroyed by giant waves.

Children write routinely for a range of tasks, purposes, and audiences. Children practice various conventions of standard English.

DIRECTIONS Write a sentence using the word below.

grind

Responses should show contextual understanding of

the word.

Write in
Response to
Reading

DIRECTIONS Revisit pp. 24–33 of *Danger! Earthquakes.* Describe the connection between two scientific ideas from this section. Use evidence from the text to support your answer.

Responses should use evidence from the text to

describe a connection between any two scientific

ideas.

Children demonstrate contextual understanding of Benchmark Vocabulary. Children read text closely and use text evidence in their written answers.

Name _____

Curtis the Cowboy Cook

Curtis was bored and unhappy. He thought when he was hired to work on the cattle drive that he'd finally get to be a real cowboy. But the cowboys treated him like a kid. The cook, Dusty, let Curtis help him. But Dusty was so busy he barely had time to talk. Curtis just watched and did chores for the cook all day long.

The chuckwagon always went ahead of the slow-moving cattle. That way, dinner would be ready when the cowboys got to camp each night. Dusty and Curtis started the cooking fire. As they carried water from a creek, Dusty slipped down the bank. He landed hard. Curtis helped Dusty limp painfully to camp. Then Curtis got to work with Dusty directing him.

He cut the salt pork and arranged it in deep pans. He scooped beans into the pans, covered them with water, and set them on the fire to boil. Soon the contents of the pans were bubbling, and the smell filled the camp. As the sun went down, the tired, hungry cowboys arrived. One bite of the hearty pork and beans was enough to convince them that Curtis was born to be a cowboy cook.

Children read text closely to determine what the text says.

Name _____

Look for Clues

Underline details that tell how the cowboys first felt about Curtis. Highlight details that tell how the cowboys' feelings changed about Curtis.

Look for Clues: Extend Your Ideas

Circle clues that tell how Curtis feels at the beginning of the story.

Ask Questions Responses will vary.

Write a question you have about cowboys.

Example: Where are you going?

Ask Questions: Extend Your Ideas

Ask a partner a question you might ask the cowboys about their actions towards Curtis. Example: Why did you treat Curtis that way?

Make Your Case

On a separate sheet of paper, list activities from the story that real cowboys do. Tell which one you think is most interesting and why.

Responses might include riding a horse.

Make Your Case: Extend Your Ideas

On a separate sheet of paper, write an e-mail to a friend about your thoughts about being a cowboy.

Name _____

DIRECTIONS Decide on a natural disaster that you would like to research. On a separate sheet of paper, take notes that answer the questions *who, what, where, when,* and *why.* Then write an informative/explanatory paragraph on the lines below that explains the answers to these questions.

Responses will vary, but the paragraph about a

natural disaster should include answers to the *who,*

what, where, when, and *why* questions.

Conventions

Adverbs Write two of your own sentences that include an adverb. Underline the adverb. Circle the verb it describes.

I. Responses will vary but should include underlined

2. adverbs and circled verbs.

Children write routinely for a range of tasks, purposes, and audiences. Children practice various conventions of standard English.

Lesson 9

Name _____

DIRECTIONS Write sentences using the words below.

collapse steep loose

Responses should show contextual understanding of the words.

Write in Response to Reading

DIRECTIONS Reread p. 31 and pp. 38–39 of *Disaster! Earthquakes*. How do the details on pp. 38–39 support the author's points on p. 31? Explain your answer using evidence from the text.

Responses will vary but should use evidence from the text including that the details reinforce the fact that earthquakes happen in the U.S.

 Children demonstrate contextual understanding of Benchmark Vocabulary. Children read text closely and use text evidence in their written answers.

Name _____

DIRECTIONS Using evidence from the text, answer the following questions about pp. 38–39 of *Danger! Earthquakes.*

1. Where do most earthquakes occur?

 Most earthquakes occur in the western part of the country.

2. What do the colors on the map mean?

 They tell where earthquakes are most common.

3. What is your favorite feature on the map? Explain why that feature is your favorite.

 Responses will vary but might include how the map key adds to the reader's understanding.

Children analyze and respond to literary and informational text.

Name _____

DIRECTIONS Write a conclusion for the natural disaster paragraph you wrote in the previous lesson.

Responses should include a relevant concluding statement.

Conventions

Adverbs Write three of your own sentences using adverbs. Use adverbs that you have not used before.

1. Responses will vary but each
2. sentence should include an
3. adverb not used previously.

Children write routinely for a range of tasks, purposes, and audiences. Children practice various conventions of standard English.

Name _____

DIRECTIONS Write a sentence using the word below.

divide

Responses should show contextual understanding of

the word.

Write in
Response to
Reading

DIRECTIONS Reread "Who Could Somersault the San Andreas Fault?" Why do you think the poet took a humorous approach to such a serious topic? Use evidence from the text to support your answer.

Responses will vary but might include that the poet

wanted to entertain his audience. He is not writing

about the fault or earthquakes.

Children demonstrate contextual understanding of Benchmark Vocabulary. Children read text closely and use text evidence in their written answers.

Name _____

DIRECTIONS Using evidence from the text, answer the following questions about "Who Could Somersault the San Andreas Fault?"

I. Why do you think poets choose to use words that rhyme?

<u>Responses might include that rhyming words</u>

<u>make the poem more fun to read.</u>

2. Why do you think the poet says, "I think *I'll* stay in bed and sleep"?

<u>Responses might include he'd rather sleep than</u>

<u>make the leap.</u>

3. Do you think there are actual road signs that say: "NO JUMPING OVER CALIFORNIA!"

<u>Responses should indicate that it is impossible to</u>

<u>jump over California.</u>

Children analyze and respond to literary and informational text.

text

Name _____

Writing

DIRECTIONS Write several sentences about a fact you have learned about one kind of natural disaster. Revisit the texts to choose a fact that interests you. Remember to clearly state the fact you are writing about. Use different words than the text uses to describe your ideas.

Responses will vary but should include facts, in the child's own words, about any natural disaster.

Conventions

Apostrophes in Contractions Rewrite each word pair as a contraction. Then write your own sentence that uses a contraction.

1. She will _She'll_ 2. They are _They're_

3. The sentence uses a contraction.

Children write routinely for a range of tasks, purposes, and audiences. Children practice various conventions of standard English.

Name _____

Diphthongs *ou, ow, oi, oy*

h**ou**se

c**ow**

c**oi**n

t**oy**

Read the name of the picture. **Circle** the word that has the same vowel sound as the name of the picture.

1.
cl**ow**n

(power)
point
pot

2.
b**oy**

(soybean)
town
robe

3.
b**oi**l

owl
(oil)
allow

4.
m**ou**se

join
loyal
(loud)

Pick a word from the box to finish each sentence.
Write the word on the line.

town
about
join
enjoy

5. We ___enjoy___ this game.

6. We are the best team in ___town___.

7. You can ___join___ us in the game.

8. We play ___about___ once a week.

Children apply grade-level phonics and word analysis skills.

Benchmark Vocabulary

DIRECTIONS Write a sentence using the word below.

grid

Responses should show contextual understanding of

the word.

> **Write in Response to Reading**

DIRECTIONS Revisit pp. 16–17 of *Disaster Alert!* and pp. 30–31 of *Danger! Earthquakes*. What do the sections of these texts have in common? Use examples from both texts to support your answer.

Responses will vary but should use evidence from

the text. Example: The photographs show holes—a

sinkhole and a hole in the road—caused by natural

disasters.

Children demonstrate contextual understanding of Benchmark Vocabulary. Children read text closely and use text evidence in their written answers.

Name _____

DIRECTIONS Choose an event from *Disaster Alert!* or *Danger! Earthquake.* Research the event to answer the questions *who, what, where, when,* and *why.* Then write your newspaper article on the lines below. Remember to include a headline that clearly states the event you are writing about.

Responses will vary but the article should include a headline and answers to the questions *who, what, when, where, and why.*

Conventions

Contractions List five contractions on the lines below.

Responses will vary but should include any five contractions.

 Children write routinely for a range of tasks, purposes, and audiences. Children practice various conventions of standard English.

Name _____

DIRECTIONS Write sentences using the words below.

collapse damage

Responses should show contextual understanding of

the words.

Write in
Response to
Reading

DIRECTIONS Think back to *Disaster Alert!* and *Danger! Earthquakes*. Which informational text is more helpful for finding information? Use evidence from both texts to support your answer.

Responses will vary. Opinions should be supported

by text evidence.

Children demonstrate contextual understanding of Benchmark Vocabulary. Children read text closely and use text evidence in their written answers.

Name _____

DIRECTIONS Write two comparison statements and two contrast statements about the text structures of *Danger! Earthquakes* and *Disaster Alert!* Revisit both texts to look for details. Use these details to support your answer.

Responses will vary but should include two comparison statements and two contrast statements. Example: Both texts explain a natural disaster and use photos, maps, diagrams, and include real-life examples. One describes many disasters; the other describes only earthquakes.

Children analyze and respond to literary and informational text.

Name _____

DIRECTIONS Revise the newspaper article you wrote in the previous lesson. Look for errors in spelling, punctuation, and capitalization. Think about information that you might like to add.

Responses will vary but include revising the article for errors and possibly adding more information.

Conventions

Contractions Write three of your own sentences that use contractions.

1. Responses will vary but

2. all three sentences should

3. include contractions.

Children write routinely for a range of tasks, purposes, and audiences. Children practice various conventions of standard English.

Name _____

Syllable Patterns

s<u>u</u>/per

s<u>up</u>/per

b<u>a</u>s/ket

p<u>a</u>/per

Pick a word from the box to match each clue.
Write the word on the line.

cowboy	magnet	picnic	blanket	painting
begin	tiger	oatmeal	boyhood	joyful

I. This is a wild animal.

2. Some people eat this for breakfast.

3. This is the same as happy.

4. A nail sticks to this.

_____tiger_____ _____oatmeal_____ _____joyful_____ _____magnet_____

5. This is when you eat outside in the park.

6. He rides a horse and herds cows.

7. This can keep you warm in bed.

8. This word is opposite of **end**.

_____picnic_____ _____cowboy_____ _____blanket_____ _____begin_____

Children apply grade-level phonics and word analysis skills.

Lesson 1

Name _____

Benchmark Vocabulary

DIRECTIONS Write sentences using the words below.

wild tangled

Responses should show contextual understanding of

the words.

Write in
Response to
Reading

DIRECTIONS Reread pp. 3–6 of *John Chapman: Planter and Pioneer.* What is the main topic of this biography? Use details from the text to support your answer.

Responses should use text evidence to support the

idea that the topic is about John planting apple trees.

Children demonstrate contextual understanding of Benchmark Vocabulary. Children read text closely and use text evidence in their written answers.

Name _____

DIRECTIONS Revisit the illustrations on pp. 3–6 of *John Chapman: Planter and Pioneer.* Write a paragraph that explains whether you think there is enough evidence to support the idea that Johnny Appleseed was an important figure. Use reasons and evidence from the text and illustrations to support your answer.

Responses will vary but should include text evidence to support the opinion.

Conventions

Apostrophes in Singular Possessives Complete the sentences below with singular possessive nouns.

1. ___His___ dad knew that he loved the outdoors.

2. ___Her___ favorite thing was the way plants grew so thick and tangled.

Children write routinely for a range of tasks, purposes, and audiences. Children practice various conventions of standard English.

Name _____

DIRECTIONS Write sentences using the words below.

amazed visitors

Responses should show contextual understanding of

the words.

DIRECTIONS Reread pp. 7–10 of *John Chapman: Planter and Pioneer.* Would you want to live back in the time of Johnny Appleseed? Use evidence from the text to support your answer.

Responses should use text evidence to support the

opinion.

Children demonstrate contextual understanding of Benchmark Vocabulary. Children read text closely and use text evidence in their written answers.

DIRECTIONS Using evidence from the text, answer the following questions about pp. 7–10 of *John Chapman: Planter and Pioneer.*

1. Reread p. 7. Where did John sleep at night?

Outside; hollowed-out tree stumps/piles of leaves

2. Reread pp. 8–10. What did John eat?

wild fruits and vegetables

3. What amazed visitors about John?

Responses will vary but could include his coffee sack coat.

4. Why did John choose to not wear shoes?

He said that shoes hurt his feet.

Children analyze and respond to literary and informational text.

DIRECTIONS Revisit pp. 7–10 of *John Chapman: Planter and Pioneer.* Write a paragraph that explores the connection between the title of the book and the unit title—Pioneering New Ideas and New Worlds. Use reasons and evidence from the text to support your answer.

Responses will vary but should include text evidence to explain the connection.

Copyright © Pearson Education, Inc., or its affiliates. All Rights Reserved.

Conventions

Apostrophes in Plural Possessives Write two of your own sentences that use plural possessives.

1. Responses will vary, but both sentences should include

2. plural possessives.

Children write routinely for a range of tasks, purposes, and audiences. Children practice various conventions of standard English.

Name _____

DIRECTIONS Write a sentence using the word below.

beneath

Responses should show contextual understanding of the word.

DIRECTIONS Reread the first paragraph on p. 15 of *John Chapman: Planter and Pioneer.* What is the main purpose of this paragraph? What details support the main purpose? Use examples from the text to support your answer.

Responses should use text evidence to support the main purpose, which is to explain why John would plant trees in the wild.

Children demonstrate contextual understanding of Benchmark Vocabulary. Children read text closely and use text evidence in their written answers.

Name _____

Journey to Freedom

In 1854, William was an African American slave in North Carolina. He longed to be free, but that did not seem possible. Late one night, a friend woke up William. He wanted William to escape with him to Canada.

The thought of freedom made William joyful. But how would he and his friend get to Canada? It was hundreds of miles away. They had very little money or food. They had no maps. Where would they hide along the way? Soldiers and other people were looking everywhere for runaway slaves. The answer to his questions was the Underground Railroad.

The Underground Railroad was not a railroad. It was a network of people. The network helped enslaved people escape to freedom. Some "conductors" on the railroad led enslaved people by foot or wagon to safe places. Other people opened their homes and barns to give shelter. Some gave money, clothes, and food to help. Before the end of slavery in the United States, thousands of people used the Underground Railroad to escape slavery.

Even with all that help, the path to freedom was not easy. The trip often took weeks. It was very dangerous. Many of the people who used the railroad agreed that the long journey was a small price to pay for freedom.

Children read text closely to determine what the text says.

Look for Clues

Tell what the word *conductor* means in this text.

a person who led a slave to safety

Look for Clues: Extend Your Ideas

Underline the meaning of *railroad* as used in the text.

Ask Questions

Write a question you have about the Underground Railroad.

Example: Who started it?

Ask Questions: Extend Your Ideas

On a sheet of paper, write a question you might ask a "conductor" of the Underground Railroad. *Example: How do you help?*

Make Your Case

Circle words that help you understand how difficult it was to escape from slavery.

On a sheet of paper, write which hardship you think would be most difficult and why. *Opinions should be supported by reasons.*

Make Your Case: Extend Your Ideas

On a sheet of paper, tell why the Underground Railroad was difficult for "conductors" as well as escaping slaves. *Responses might include because it was dangerous.*

Children read text closely to determine what the text says.

Name _____

DIRECTIONS Write a paragraph about why you think it is important to live by example. Revisit *John Chapman: Planter and Pioneer* to find evidence that supports your opinion. Remember to introduce your topic in an interesting way, and to end your paragraph by summarizing your ideas.

Responses will vary but should use text evidence

to support the opinion. The paragraph should

have an interesting beginning and should end by

summarizing the evidence.

Conventions

Apostrophes Circle the possessive nouns. Then write your own sentence that uses an apostrophe.

1. (children's) (teacher's) can't (doctors') she'll

2. Responses will vary but the sentence should

include a possessive noun with an apostrophe.

Children write routinely for a range of tasks, purposes, and audiences. Children practice various conventions of standard English.

Name _____

DIRECTIONS Write sentences using the words below.

clever planter tattered

Responses should show contextual understanding of the words.

Write in
Response to
Reading

DIRECTIONS Reread p. 19 of *John Chapman: Planter and Pioneer*. What reasons does the author provide to support the idea that John was a clever man? Use examples from the text to support your answer.

Responses should use text evidence including that Johnny knew right where the settlers wanted to live.

Children demonstrate contextual understanding of Benchmark Vocabulary. Children read text closely and use text evidence in their written answers.

DIRECTIONS Using evidence from the text, answer the following questions about pp. 17–23 of *John Chapman: Planter and Pioneer.*

1. Reread p. 19. What reason does the author provide to support the idea that John worked hard?

He walked hundreds of miles.

2. Reread pp. 20–21. List four reasons the author provides to support the idea that John's home "was still the great outdoors."

Reason 1: He ate wild foods.

Reason 2: He built fires to cook and stay warm.

Reason 3: He slept outdoors.

Reason 4: Nature met his needs.

3. Reread p. 22. Why did John sometimes get cold?

His clothes were thin and tattered.

Children analyze and respond to literary and informational text.

DIRECTIONS Reread pp. 17–23 of *John Chapman: Planter and Pioneer.* Write a paragraph that answers the following question: Was Johnny Appleseed a hero? Explain why or why not. Use linking words to connect your opinion and reasons. Revisit the text for examples to support your answer.

Responses will vary but should use text evidence

to support the opinion. The paragraph should include

linking words.

Conventions

Possessive Pronouns Write your own sentences that use two of the following possessive pronouns: *her, hers; their, theirs; our, ours.*

1. Each sentence should include one possessive

2. pronoun listed above.

Children write routinely for a range of tasks, purposes, and audiences. Children practice various conventions of standard English.

DIRECTIONS Write sentences using the words below.

hero creatures legend

Responses should show contextual understanding of the words.

Write in
Response to
Reading

DIRECTIONS Reread p. 31 of *John Chapman: Planter and Pioneer.* How does the text on this page contribute to the author's purpose? Use evidence from the text to support your answer.

Responses should include that the text reinforces the purpose of telling about the life of John Chapman.

 Children demonstrate contextual understanding of Benchmark Vocabulary. Children read text closely and use text evidence in their written answers.

Name _____

DIRECTIONS Using evidence from the text, answer the following questions about pp. 24–32 of *John Chapman: Planter and Pioneer.*

1. Reread p. 25. What is the meaning of the word *cubs*?

baby bears

2. What could help you find out the meaning if you did not know it?

look at the illustration/dictionary

3. Reread p. 28. What is the meaning of the word *superman*?

a strong person, or someone doing amazing things

4. What words or phrases does the author use to support the idea above?

Responses will vary but should include "chopping wood quickly" or "walking twice as fast."

 Children analyze and respond to literary and informational text.

Name _____

DIRECTIONS Write a letter to a friend that gives your opinion about whether or not you believe one of the stories in the book *John Chapman: Planter and Pioneer.* Remember to tell your friend why you are writing to them. Revisit the text to find examples and details to support your opinion.

Responses will vary but the letter should use text evidence to support the opinion.

Conventions

Possessive Pronouns Write your own sentences that use two of the following possessive pronouns: *mine, hers, his, theirs, ours.*

1. Sentences should include one

2. possessive pronoun listed above.

Children write routinely for a range of tasks, purposes, and audiences. Children practice various conventions of standard English.

Name _____

Vowel Digraphs *oo, ue, ew, ui*

m**oo**n gl**ue** scr**ew** fr**ui**t

Circle the word that has the same vowel sound as **moon**.
Write the word on the line.

1. uncut (untrue) unplug	2. (grew) grow grain
__untrue__	__grew__
3. stood (spoon) spun	4. just joy (juice)
__spoon__	__juice__

Circle a word to finish each sentence. **Choose** a word that has the same vowel sound as **new**.

5. I _____ home from Roy's house on a plane.

 flow fun (flew)

6. I just unpacked my _____.

 sudden (suitcase) supper

7. I want to _____ the library book about cows.

 (renew) repeat recess

Children apply grade-level phonics and word analysis skills.

Name _____

Benchmark Vocabulary

DIRECTIONS Write sentences using the words below.

stretch thankful

Responses should show contextual understanding of

the words.

Write in
Response to
Reading

DIRECTIONS Revisit pp. 3–32 of *John Chapman: Planter and Pioneer*. Write about the part of Johnny Appleseed's life that you most admire. Use evidence from the text to support your answer.

Responses will vary but should use text evidence to

support the opinion.

Children demonstrate contextual understanding of Benchmark Vocabulary. Children read text closely and use text evidence in their written answers.

Name _____

DIRECTIONS Write an opinion about whether or not you think Johnny Appleseed's work made our world a better place. Remember to clearly state an opinion and support it with reasons. You should also provide a well-developed conclusion.

Responses will vary but should use text evidence to

support the opinion. Example: Johnny planted many

apple trees, which helped to make the world a better

place for the settlers.

Conventions

Simple Sentences Write simple sentences using the given subjects and verbs below.

1. girl played

Sentences should include the listed subjects and

2. they walked

verbs.

Children write routinely for a range of tasks, purposes, and audiences. Children practice various conventions of standard English.

Lesson 7

Name _____

Benchmark Vocabulary

DIRECTIONS Write a sentence using the word below.

settlers

Responses should show contextual understanding of the word.

DIRECTIONS Revisit pp. 51–69 of *Johnny Appleseed.*
What kinds of information would you add to the timeline?
Explain why you would add this information. Use examples
from the text to support your answer.

Responses will vary but should use text evidence

to support events added to the timeline. Example:

1794–1797: Johnny continues walking west.

Children demonstrate contextual understanding of
Benchmark Vocabulary. Children read text closely and
use text evidence in their written answers.

Name _____

DIRECTIONS Revisit pp. 64–65 of *Johnny Appleseed.* Which text feature in this section do you think is more informative—the timeline or the caption? Use evidence from the text to support your answer.

Responses will vary but might include that the caption offers more information because it tells that Johnny read to the settlers.

Children analyze and respond to literary and informational text.

Name _____

DIRECTIONS Write an opinion paragraph that states whether using the timeline helped you understand the text. State your opinion clearly and give reasons that support that opinion. Use linking words and phrases to connect ideas. Remember to include a concluding statement.

Responses will vary but should use text evidence

to support the opinion. The paragraph should use

linking verbs and phrases and include a concluding

statement.

Conventions

Expand Simple Sentences Add adjectives to the simple sentences below.

1. John wanted to see the frontier.

Sentences should include at least one adjective.

2. He liked to play in the woods.

Examples: *wide-open frontier* and *dark woods.*

Children write routinely for a range of tasks, purposes, and audiences. Children practice various conventions of standard English.

Name _____

DIRECTIONS Write a sentence using the word below.

orchards

Responses should show contextual understanding of

the word.

Write in Response to Reading

DIRECTIONS Reread pp. 56–57 of *Johnny Appleseed.* What text features does the author provide that help you locate facts? Use examples from the text to support your answer.

illustration, time line, and caption

Children demonstrate contextual understanding of Benchmark Vocabulary. Children read text closely and use text evidence in their written answers.

Name _____

DIRECTIONS On a separate sheet of paper, write an opinion that states whether you would add headings to the text. Or, do you think the time line gives you enough information about what is on the page? Use linking words such as *and, because,* and *also* to connect your opinion and reasons. Remember to provide a concluding statement.

Responses will vary but should include reasons for

the opinion, using linking words. The opinion paper

should have a concluding statement.

Conventions

Expand Simple Sentences Add an adverb to the simple sentences below. Sentences should include adverbs.

1. He _____ walked around the country planting apple trees.

2. John _____ collected apple seeds from cider mills.

Children write routinely for a range of tasks, purposes, and audiences. Children practice various conventions of standard English.

Name _____

DIRECTIONS Write a sentence using the word below.

nickname

Responses should show contextual understanding of

the word.

Write in Response to Reading

DIRECTIONS Reread pp. 62–69 of *Johnny Appleseed.* How did Johnny Appleseed help settlers and the land? Do you think these reasons are strong enough to remember him so many years later? Use examples from the text to support your answer.

Responses should use text evidence, including

examples, to support the opinion.

Children demonstrate contextual understanding of Benchmark Vocabulary. Children read text closely and use text evidence in their written answers.

Name _____

DIRECTIONS The message on John Chapman's gravestone reads: *He lived for others.* Revisit the text and find three or four reasons that support the message on his gravestone. Write these reasons on the lines below. Use evidence from the text.

Responses will vary but should include evidence from the text. Example: John helped the settlers plant orchards. He shared apple seeds, apple trees, and stories.

Children analyze and respond to literary and informational text.

Name _____

DIRECTIONS Revisit p. 68 of *Johnny Appleseed* and reread the message on John Chapman's gravestone. Write an opinion statement about whether or not you agree with the message. If you agree, then explain why. If you do not, then tell what message you would put instead and why. Use linking words such as *because, and,* and *also* to connect opinions. Remember to provide a concluding statement.

Responses will vary but should include reasons

to support the opinion. Responses should include

linking words and a concluding statement.

Expand Simple Sentences Combine the simple sentences below into one sentence with a compound subject. Then write your own sentence with a compound subject.

1. Marta planted flowers. Josie planted flowers.

Marta and Josie planted flowers.

2. _Sentence should have a compound subject._

Children write routinely for a range of tasks, purposes, and audiences. Children practice various conventions of standard English.

Name _____

DIRECTIONS Write a sentence using the word below.

frontier

Responses should show contextual understanding of
the word.

Write in
Response to
Reading

DIRECTIONS Revisit pp. 62–63 of *Johnny Appleseed.*
How does the information in this section support the text's
main purpose? Use examples from the text to support your
answer.

Responses should use text evidence including that

the information gives facts about Johnny's life,

which is the purpose of the text.

Children demonstrate contextual understanding of
Benchmark Vocabulary. Children read text closely and
use text evidence in their written answers.

Name _____

DIRECTIONS Using evidence from the text, answer the following question about pp. 51–69 of *Johnny Appleseed.*

I. Think about the main purpose of *Johnny Appleseed.* Then write a paragraph about the text's main purpose and the details that support it. Use text evidence to support your opinion.

Responses will vary but should use text evidence to

support the purpose of the text, which is to tell about

the life of John Chapman. Paragraphs should include

facts stated in the text, such as when John was born,

where he traveled, and how he helped the settlers.

Children analyze and respond to literary and informational text.

Name _____

DIRECTIONS You will write an opinion piece about which book you feel is more informative about John Chapman's life—*John Chapman: Planter and Pioneer* or *Johnny Appleseed.* Use the Venn diagram from Writing Workshop to make a list of points that you can use in your opinion piece. Then, on a separate sheet of paper, write an opinion statement about the text you think is more informative.

Responses will vary but should use some points in

the Venn diagram to support the opinion.

Conventions

Expand Simple Sentences Combine the simple sentences below into a single sentence with a compound verb. Then write your own sentence that uses a compound verb.

I. John gave apple seeds. John sold apple seeds.

John gave and sold apple seeds.

2. Sentence should use a compound verb.

Children write routinely for a range of tasks, purposes, and audiences. Children practice various conventions of standard English.

Name _____

Suffixes *-ly, -ful, -er, -or, -ish*

teach + *er* = teach**er** sail + *or* = sail**or** child + *ish* = child**ish**

**Add *-er, -or,* or *-ish* to each word to make a word.
Write the new word on the line.**

visit

1. visitor

fool

2. foolish

sing

3. singer

act

4. actor

self

5. selfish

help

6. helper

slow + *ly* = slow**ly** cheer + *ful* = cheer**ful**

**Add *-ly* or *-ful* to each word to make a new word.
Write the new word on the line.**

week

7. weekly

joy

8. joyful

quick

9. quickly

hope

10. hopeful

Children apply grade-level phonics and word analysis skills.

Name _____

Benchmark Vocabulary

DIRECTIONS Write sentences using the words below.

boughs drowsy

Responses should show contextual understanding of

the words.

**Write in
Response to
Reading**

DIRECTIONS Reread "Planting a Tree" and "Trees" on pp. 118–119. Why would a poet repeat lines in a poem? Do you think repetition in a poem makes it better? Use examples from the text to support your answer.

Responses will vary but might include an opinion

that the repetition adds emphasis and makes the

poem better.

Children demonstrate contextual understanding of Benchmark Vocabulary. Children read text closely and use text evidence in their written answers.

DIRECTIONS Revisit the list of points you would like to include in your opinion piece. On a separate sheet of paper, write a draft of your opinion about which book you feel is more informative about John Chapman's life — *John Chapman: Planter and Pioneer* or *Johnny Appleseed*. Remember to use linking words to connect your opinions and reasons.

Responses will vary but should include a draft of the opinion and linking words to connect the opinion and the reasons.

Conventions

Rearrange Simple Sentences Rearrange the words in the simple sentences below.

1. In 1838, John moved to Indiana.

John moved to Indiana in 1838.

2. He was given the name Johnny Appleseed by settlers.

Settlers gave him the name Johnny Appleseed.

Children write routinely for a range of tasks, purposes, and audiences. Children practice various conventions of standard English.

Name _____

DIRECTIONS Write sentences using the words below.

wild hero

Responses should show contextual understanding of

the words.

Write in Response to Reading

DIRECTIONS Which text do you like more—*John Chapman: Planter and Pioneer* or *Johnny Appleseed*? Explain why. Use evidence from the text to support your answer.

Responses will vary but should use text evidence

from the preferred text to support the opinion.

Children demonstrate contextual understanding of Benchmark Vocabulary. Children read text closely and use text evidence in their written answers.

DIRECTIONS Write three ways that *John Chapman: Planter and Pioneer* and *Johnny Appleseed* are similar. Then explain how the texts are different. Use evidence from both texts to support your answer.

Responses will vary but might include that both texts are about Johnny Appleseed, both are factual, and both use illustrations. One text uses a time line and captions, while the other text gives more details about Johnny Appleseed.

Children analyze and respond to literary and informational text.

Name _____

DIRECTIONS Think of ways to improve the draft of your opinion piece about the book you feel is more informative about John Chapman's life—*John Chapman: Planter and Pioneer* or *Johnny Appleseed.* Add linking words to make the connections between opinions, reasons, and ideas stronger. Rearrange sentences to add interest and variety. Include a concluding statement or section to wrap up your ideas. Revise your writing on a separate sheet of paper.

Children revise their drafts by rearranging sentences and adding a concluding statement.

Conventions

Expand and Rearrange Sentences Rewrite the sentences below by rearranging and expanding them.

1. The other night we sat in our backyard. We watched falling stars. We saw about a dozen of them.

 Sentences should be rearranged and expanded

 correctly.

2. He walked along the country road. He stopped to plant apple trees. He stopped to speak with settlers.

 Sentences should be rearranged and expanded

 correctly.

Children write routinely for a range of tasks, purposes, and audiences. Children practice various conventions of standard English.

Name _____

DIRECTIONS Write sentences using the words below.

planter orchards

Responses should show contextual understanding of

the words.

Write in
Response to
Reading

DIRECTIONS Revisit *John Chapman: Planter and Pioneer* and *Johnny Appleseed*. Write several reasons why authors include different material when writing about the same topic. Use evidence from the text to support your answer.

Responses might include how each author focuses

on different aspects of the topic and presents the

material in his or her own way, such as by using a

time line to summarize the text.

Children demonstrate contextual understanding of
Benchmark Vocabulary. Children read text closely
and use text evidence in their written answers.

Lesson 13

Name _____

Sleuth Work

A Journey North

Harlem is a very interesting place. In the early 1900s many African Americans headed north. They left the South to find a new life in the North. Many settled in Harlem. Harlem is a neighborhood in New York City.

Life in the South had been hard. There were few jobs. The North had more jobs and the chance of a better life.

African Americans hoped they would get jobs in factories in the North. They dreamt of making more money. They wanted better schools for their children.

Most African Americans lived in the South. Their journey north changed that. More than half of all African Americans moved from the South. However, some had never lived in cities. Cities were big and noisy. It was difficult to live in a new place. Many found comfort living in neighborhoods with other African Americans.

Harlem became the largest African American neighborhood in the country. A group of artists, musicians, and singers used their talents to show African American culture. Palmer Hayden painted paintings of African Americans in the South and the North. Other artists sang songs or wrote about their experiences. They shared the journeys of African Americans with America.

Children read text closely to determine what the text says.

Name _____

Look for Clues

Underline clues in the selection that tell why people moved to Harlem.

Look for Clues: Extend Your Ideas

Circle a reason why people moved from the South to the North.

Ask Questions

Write a question that you have about Harlem after reading this selection. **Responses will vary.**

Example: What is the title of one song?

Ask Questions: Extend Your Ideas

Write a question to ask Palmer Hayden. **Responses will vary.**

Example: Are real people shown in your paintings?

Make Your Case

Which piece of information in the selection makes Harlem seem most interesting to you? **Responses will vary. Example:**

Harlem was the biggest African American neighborhood.

Make Your Case: Extend Your Ideas

On a sheet of paper, write a headline for a newspaper article about Harlem. **Responses will vary.**

Example: A Great Neighborhood

Children read text closely to determine what the text says.

Name _____

DIRECTIONS Use the Editing Checklist to edit your revised drafts. You may want to use different colored pencils to mark your corrections. Remember that you can use a dictionary to check the spelling of any words you are unsure of. On a separate sheet of paper, publish or print your final draft.

Children should edit and then publish their work.

Rearrange Simple and Compound Sentences Rewrite the sentences below by rearranging and expanding them.

We went to the apple orchard. I picked Red Delicious apples. My mom picked Golden Delicious apples. My brother went through the corn maze.

Responses will vary. Example: Last week, we drove to the apple orchard. While Mom and I picked apples, my little brother got lost in the corn maze.

Children write routinely for a range of tasks, purposes, and audiences. Children practice various conventions of standard English.

Name _____

Prefixes *un-*, *re-*, *pre-*, *dis-*

un + happy = **un**happy *dis* + regard = **dis**regard
re + paint = **re**paint *pre* + game = **pre**game

disagree	disloyal	disregard	reapply	prepay
preteen	replay	reread	unsafe	unlocked

Write words with ***un-*, *re-*, *pre-*,** or ***dis-*** to match each clue.

Use the words in the box if you need help.

1. play again **replay**	**2.** not agree **disagree**
3. not regard **disregard**	**4.** pay in advance **prepay**
5. not locked **unlocked**	**6.** not loyal **disloyal**
7. not yet a teen **preteen**	**8.** apply again **reapply**
9. not safe **unsafe**	**10.** read again **reread**

Children apply grade-level phonics and word analysis skills.

Name _____

DIRECTIONS Write sentences using the words below.

conflict fortune

Responses should show contextual understanding of

the words.

DIRECTIONS Reread pp. 1–9 of *Pioneers to the West*. Why do you think the author used different types of paper for different text feature boxes throughout the book? Use evidence from the text to support your answer.

Responses will vary but might include that Bliss

wanted each feature to stand out. Repeating features

are on the same style of paper.

Children demonstrate contextual understanding of Benchmark Vocabulary. Children read text closely and use text evidence in their written answers.

DIRECTIONS Think about what you have read in *Pioneers to the West.* Then make connections between the title of the text and the title of the unit—Pioneering New Ideas and New Worlds. Write a story in which you are a pioneer traveling across the country in search of a new opportunity. Use facts and details from the text to support your story.

Responses will vary but might include that the text

is about pioneers who settle in a new place, which is

an example of why the text fits with the unit title.

Conventions

Use Simple Sentences Underline the subject in each sentence.

1. The <u>family</u> moved west on a covered wagon.

2. <u>George Staples</u> was born in England.

Children write routinely for a range of tasks, purposes, and audiences. Children practice various conventions of standard English.

Name _____

DIRECTIONS Write sentences using the words below.

bound typical

Responses should show contextual understanding of

the words.

DIRECTIONS Reread pp. 10–11 of *Pioneers to the West*.
What caused so many people to flock to California in 1849?
Use evidence from the text to support your answer.

Responses will vary but should use text evidence

including that gold was found on John Sutter's

property. People went with the hope of finding gold.

Children demonstrate contextual understanding of
Benchmark Vocabulary. Children read text closely and
use text evidence in their written answers.

Name _____

DIRECTIONS Using evidence from the text, answer the following question about pp. 10–13 of *Pioneers to the West*.

I. Reread pp. 10–13. Select an event that happened and reasons for why that event happened. Write a few sentences that explain what happened and why. Remember to use signal words such as *because* to help you explain why the event happened.

Responses will vary. Examples might include

that people flocked to California to find gold; John

McWilliams found $100 worth of gold in one day,

but his good luck did not hold; Levi Strauss made a

fortune by making pants that could hold up to the

tough lives of miners.

Children analyze and respond to literary and informational text.

DIRECTIONS Think about what you read in *Pioneers to the West* about the life of John McWilliams, and the most important events that happened to him. How might the chart you worked on help you to write a narrative about John McWilliams?

John McWilliams found $100 worth of gold in one day, but his luck did not hold. John then traveled to Panama, to New Orleans, and finally to St. Louis. The chart might help readers make connections between events.

Conventions

Prepositional Phrases Underline the prepositional phrase in the sentence below. Then write your own sentence that uses a prepositional phrase.

I. The inspector found gold at the sawmill.

2. The sentence should have a prepositional phrase.

Children write routinely for a range of tasks, purposes, and audiences. Children practice various conventions of standard English.

Name _____

DIRECTIONS Write sentences using the words below.

territory opportunities

Responses should show contextual understanding of

the words.

DIRECTIONS Reread pp. 14–19 of *Pioneers to the West*. How does asking and answering questions help you understand what you read? Use evidence from the text to support your answer.

Responses will vary but might include that asking

and answering questions helps you better

understand and remember what you are reading.

Children demonstrate contextual understanding of Benchmark Vocabulary. Children read text closely and use text evidence in their written answers.

DIRECTIONS Using evidence from the text, answer the following questions about pp. 14–19 of *Pioneers to the West*.

1. What is a temporal word?

A temporal word signals the time something

happens.

2. Reread the first paragraph on p. 16. What temporal word is used?

After

3. Reread the first paragraph on p. 17. What temporal word is used?

When

4. How do the temporal words help you understand what is happening in this section?

Responses will vary but might include that the words

help you follow the sequence of events.

Children analyze and respond to literary and informational text.

Name _____

DIRECTIONS Consider what you read about Laura Ingalls Wilder in *Pioneers to the West*. Use a Story Sequence Chart to help you plan a narrative about her childhood. Identify the characters and setting of your narrative. Then write several sentences about how the planning chart will help you write your narrative.

Children complete a Story Sequence Chart about

Laura's childhood. Their sentences might point out

how the chart helps them put events in order.

Prepositional Phrases Underline the prepositional phrases that tell **when** something happened.

On Wednesday, Patty and Maddie looked out the window. Rain fell. In April, it had rained a lot. The girls wanted to play before it rained again.

Children write routinely for a range of tasks, purposes, and audiences. Children practice various conventions of standard English.

Name _____

DIRECTIONS Write a sentence using the word below.

blizzard

Responses should show contextual understanding of

the word.

Write in
Response to
Reading

DIRECTIONS Do you think the advertisement on p. 20 of *Pioneers to the West* would convince your family to move west? Use evidence from the text to support your answer.

Responses will vary but might include that the

advertisement would be convincing because it says

you can get land on credit for 10 years.

Children demonstrate contextual understanding of Benchmark Vocabulary. Children read text closely and use text evidence in their written answers.

Name _____

DIRECTIONS Look at the photograph on p. 23 of *Pioneers to the West*. Write the main idea of this photograph. Then write the key details that are found in the photo's caption.

Main Idea:

Children went west on orphan trains.

Key Details:

The orphan trains carried more than 100,000 children west between 1854 and 1929.

Children analyze and respond to literary and informational text.

Name _____

DIRECTIONS On a separate sheet of paper, write the first draft of your narrative about Laura Ingalls Wilder. Your narrative should follow the events outlined on your Story Sequence Chart. Include details about Laura's thoughts, feelings, words, and actions to help readers understand Laura's character better. Return to the text to gather facts about Laura's childhood.

Responses will vary but narratives should use the events outlined in the chart.

Conventions

Prepositional Phrases Add a prepositional phrase to the sentence below. Then write your own sentences that use prepositional phrases.

1. Ruth Chrisman saved her students Children should

2. complete Sentence 1 with a prepositional phrase.

Sentences 2 and 3 should include prepositional

3. phrases.

Children write routinely for a range of tasks, purposes, and audiences. Children practice various conventions of standard English.

DIRECTIONS Write sentences using the words below.

destiny progress

Responses should show contextual understanding of

the words.

Write in
Response to
Reading

DIRECTIONS Reread pp. 26–29 of *Pioneers to the West*. Explain a connection between two historical events discussed in this section. Use evidence from the text to support your answer.

Responses should use text evidence including that

settling the western lands forced American Indians

off their lands. The map shows the setters' routes

and the American Indians' route to the reservations.

Children demonstrate contextual understanding of
Benchmark Vocabulary. Children read text closely and
use text evidence in their written answers.

Name _____

DIRECTIONS Reread pp. 26–27 of *Pioneers to the West.* Write a paragraph that describes the connection between Manifest Destiny and the Trail of Tears. Use evidence from the text to support your answer.

Responses will vary but should use text evidence showing the connection. The country's Manifest Destiny was to stretch from the Atlantic Ocean to the Pacific Ocean. This destiny came at a price. Thousands of American Indians were forced off their land and onto reservations. Their journey became known as the Trail of Tears.

Children analyze and respond to literary and informational text.

DIRECTIONS Identify and describe a connection between the Homestead Act and another event in *Pioneers to the West*.

Responses will vary but might include the connection

between the act and the Chrisman sisters claiming

their own land.

Conventions

Prepositional Phrases Expand the simple sentences below by adding prepositional phrases.

I. A person just had to be 21 years old.

Example: A person just had to be 21 years old to

own land.

2. Ruth started teaching school.

Example: In the fall, Ruth started teaching school.

Children write routinely for a range of tasks, purposes, and audiences. Children practice various conventions of standard English.

Consonant Patterns *kn, wr, gn, mb*

knee **wr**ist si**gn** la**mb**

Say the word for each picture.

Write kn, wr, gn, or **mb** to finish each word.

1. 2. 3. 4.

wrench co**mb** **kn**ob **gn**at

5. 6. 7. 8.

cli**mb** **wr**ite **kn**ock thu**mb**

Find the word that has the same beginning sound as the picture.

Mark the space to show your answer.

9. ☒ wrong 10. ☐ king
 ☐ wing ☒ knife
 ☐ white ☐ kick

 Children apply grade-level phonics and word analysis skills.

Name _____

DIRECTIONS Write a sentence using the word below.

advertisements

Responses should show contextual understanding of

the word.

Write in
Response to
Reading

DIRECTIONS Reread pp. 4–5 and 26–29 of *Pioneers of the West*. Select one of the images and tell what you learned from it. How does it contribute to the text? Use evidence from the text to support your answer.

Responses will vary but should tell how the selected

image contributes to the text.

Children demonstrate contextual understanding of Benchmark Vocabulary. Children read text closely and use text evidence in their written answers.

DIRECTIONS Return to your Laura Ingalls Wilder narrative. Plan some illustrations that you want to include with your narrative, noting why each one would be useful to the reader. List the main event of your narrative and the kinds of illustrations you want to include. Then write a short description and caption for each illustration. Write your plan on a separate sheet of paper.

Children write descriptions of illustrations and captions for their narratives.

Conventions

Rearrange Simple Sentences Rewrite the sentences below in a new way.

I. The pioneers found gold in California.

In California, the pioneers found gold.

2. But this destiny came at a price.

This destiny came at a price.

3. Those who refused to leave faced the force of the U.S. Army.

The U.S. Army forced people to leave.

Children write routinely for a range of tasks, purposes, and audiences. Children practice various conventions of standard English.

DIRECTIONS Write a sentence using the word below.

swaying

Responses should show contextual understanding of

the word.

Write in
Response to
Reading

DIRECTIONS Reread p. 75 of *Going West*. Whose point of view do you most agree with — Mama's or Papa's? Why? Use examples from the text to support your answer.

Responses will vary but should use text evidence to

explain the chosen point of view.

Children demonstrate contextual understanding of Benchmark Vocabulary. Children read text closely and use text evidence in their written answers.

DIRECTIONS Reread pp. 71–85. Choose two characters and identify the challenges they faced. Then explain how each character responded to those challenges. Use evidence from the text.

Responses will vary but should include text evidence to identify the challenges faced by any two characters and how each responded to those challenges.

Children analyze and respond to literary and informational text.

Name _____

DIRECTIONS Revisit pp. 71–85 in *Going West*. Flag evidence in the text that helps you understand Mama's or Jake's point of view about the journey west. On a separate sheet of paper, write a statement that summarizes Mama's or Jake's point of view. Then write a new beginning from Mama's or Jake's point of view on the lines below.

Responses will vary. Examples: Mama cried because

she was leaving family and furniture. Jake cried and

said he wanted to go home. Children should write a

beginning from either character's point of view.

Conventions

Rearrange Simple Sentences Rewrite the sentence below in a new way.

1. We were all tired of the rocking wagon and the dust.

Responses will vary. Example: All of us were tired

of the dusty, bumpy wagon ride.

 Children write routinely for a range of tasks, purposes, and audiences. Children practice various conventions of standard English.

Name _____

DIRECTIONS Write sentences using the words below.

baking shriveling squashed

Responses should show contextual understanding of

the words.

Write in
Response to
Reading

DIRECTIONS Reread pp. 96–98 of *Going West*. How do the details in this section support the central message of the text? Use details from the text to support your answer.

Responses will vary but should use text evidence

including that the family moved because Papa said

anything they planted would grow, and he wants to

plant again.

Children demonstrate contextual understanding of Benchmark Vocabulary. Children read text closely and use text evidence in their written answers.

Name _____

From Seed to Flower to Fruit

Do you know where apples come from? Have you ever seen an apple **seed**? Inside that tiny brown shell is the beginning of a whole new tree.

Every seed contains an **embryo**, or a baby plant. The seed protects the baby plant. Then when the seed gets the right amount of water and warmth, it breaks open. The embryo begins to grow.

A **stem** with little seed **leaves** pushes upward. There may be one leaf or two leaves. The **seedling** wants light to help it grow. **Roots** also begin to grow. They help the seedling get the food from the soil.

New leaves grow from the stem. When there are enough new leaves, the seed leaves fall off. Soon, **flower buds** appear. When the flowers open, bees move pollen from one flower to another. New seeds form inside the flower.

The part of the plant where these seeds are grows larger. It becomes a tiny **apple**, and soon it will be ready to eat. Do you see the seeds inside? Each seed is ready for a chance to become a new plant. The cycle begins again!

Look for Clues

Turn to a partner and tell why some words are in bolder print and how that helps you as you read.

Look for Clues: Extend Your Ideas

Using clues from the text, tell a partner what the word *seed* means.

Seed means "tiny brown shell."

Ask Questions

Write a question that you would ask a gardener if you planned on growing an apple tree. **Responses will vary.**

Example: How much water do I use?

Make Your Case

On a sheet of paper, draw an apple tree and label it. Then write which part of the growing process you think is most interesting.

Responses should include which part of the growing process the child finds most interesting.

Make Your Case: Extend Your Ideas

In the article, underline the terms that you should include in your picture.

Possibilities are underlined in the article.

Children read text closely to determine what the text says.

Name _____

DIRECTIONS Revisit the class's narrative scene and consider where the writing might change in order to write the scene from Mama's or Papa's point of view. Then rewrite the scene from the point of view of Mama or Papa.

Responses will vary but should include text evidence

to rewrite the scene from the character's point of

view.

Conventions

Combining Sentences Combine the simple sentences below into compound sentences.

1. Sam set the table. Mom cooked dinner.

Sam set the table, and Mom cooked the dinner.

2. The storm was over. The crops were smashed.

The storm was over, but the crops were smashed.

Children write routinely for a range of tasks, purposes, and audiences.
Children practice various conventions of standard English.

Lesson 9

Benchmark Vocabulary

Name _____

DIRECTIONS Write sentences using the words below.

stable howling

Responses should show contextual understanding of

the words.

Write in
Response to
Reading

DIRECTIONS Reread p. 107 of *Going West*. What kind of weather is the family experiencing? Use specific details and evidence from the text to support your answer.

Responses will vary but should use text evidence

including that it snowed for three days and nights.

Children demonstrate contextual understanding of Benchmark Vocabulary. Children read text closely and use text evidence in their written answers.

Name _____

DIRECTIONS Using evidence from the text, answer the following question about pp. 100–117 of *Going West*.

1. Reread p. 117. Write a paragraph that tells how the events of the beginning and middle of the story affect how you feel about the ending. Use examples from the text to support your answer.

Responses will vary but might include that the family had such a hard time that it was nice to hear that the house finally felt like home.

Name _____

DIRECTIONS Write a narrative about a child who wants to be a pioneer. Your narrative should have a beginning, middle, and end. Include at least three prepositional phrases and specific details that describe characters and events.

Responses will vary but should be about a child who

wants to be a pioneer. The narrative has a beginning,

a middle, and an end. It has three prepositional

phrases and specific details that describe characters

and events.

Conventions

Prepositional Phrases Write a sentence using one of the prepositions below.

through in on under above

Responses should include one of the prepositions

above.

 Children write routinely for a range of tasks, purposes, and audiences. Children practice various conventions of standard English.

DIRECTIONS Write sentences using the words below.

constant mounds

Responses should show contextual understanding of

the words.

Write in
Response to
Reading

DIRECTIONS Revisit *Going West*. Why is it important for people living today to understand the life of pioneers? How does this relate to the central message of the text? Use evidence from the text to explain your thoughts.

Responses will vary but should use text evidence

including that the pioneers suffered hardships to

settle the country.

Children demonstrate contextual understanding of Benchmark Vocabulary. Children read text closely and use text evidence in their written answers.

DIRECTIONS Reread pp. 116–117 of *Going West*. Tell what the central message of the text is. Then explain how the story's conclusion contributes to the central message. Use details and evidence from the text to support your answer.

Responses will vary but should use text evidence including that, after all the struggles, the family finally feels like their new place is home.

Children analyze and respond to literary and informational text.

Name _____

DIRECTIONS Revise your narrative from the previous lesson.

Responses will vary. Children revise their narratives.

Conventions

Expand Sentences Expand the sentence by adding adjectives or adverbs to it.

I. The children ran to see the piglets.

Responses will vary but the sentence should include

adverbs or adjectives.

Children write routinely for a range of tasks, purposes, and audiences. Children practice various conventions of standard English.

Consonant Patterns *ph, gh, ck, ng*

phone cou**gh** clo**ck** ri**ng**

| backpack elephant laughter trophy |
| ticket hanger graph photo dolphin |

Pick a word from the box to match each clue.
Write the word on the line.

1.

 trophy

2.

 elephant

3.

 laughter

4.

 ticket

5.

 dolphin

6.

 hanger

Pick a word from the box above to finish each sentence.
Write the word on the line.

7. Roy wears a backpack .

8. Sue is taking a photo of Roy.

Children apply grade-level phonics and word analysis skills.

DIRECTIONS Write sentences using the words below.

territory destiny

Responses should show contextual understanding of the words.

Write in
Response to
Reading

DIRECTIONS Which text do you like more—*Pioneers to the West* or *Going West*? Explain why. Use evidence from the text to support your answer.

Responses will vary but should use text evidence to support the opinion.

 Children demonstrate contextual understanding of Benchmark Vocabulary. Children read text closely and use text evidence in their written answers.

Name _____

DIRECTIONS Write a first draft of your pioneer narrative. Remember that it is fine to change things in the Story Sequence Map or Character Web if you have new ideas while you write. Use details to describe characters' thoughts, actions, and feelings.

Responses should include a first draft of the pioneer

narrative, using details to describe characters'

thoughts, actions, and feelings.

Conventions

Rearrange Sentences Write two more interesting sentences about the family's vacation.

1. Responses will vary, but the sentences should

2. be about the family's vacation.

Children write routinely for a range of tasks, purposes, and audiences. Children practice various conventions of standard English.

Name _____

DIRECTIONS Write a sentence using the word below.

progress

Responses should show contextual understanding of the word.

Write in Response to Reading

DIRECTIONS What kind of text do you most like to read—informational or narrative? Use evidence from *Pioneers to the West* and *Going West* to support your answer.

Responses will vary but should use text evidence

to support the opinion about whether a narrative or

an informational text is preferred.

Children demonstrate contextual understanding of Benchmark Vocabulary. Children read text closely and use text evidence in their written answers.

DIRECTIONS In which text do you find the images most helpful—*Pioneers to the West* or *Going West?* Explain why. Use evidence from both texts to support your answer.

Responses will vary. If *Pioneers to the West* is preferred, responses might say that the images added additional factual information to the text. If *Going West* is preferred, responses might tell how each image illustrated the text on that page and helped readers understand what they were reading.

Children analyze and respond to literary and informational text.

DIRECTIONS Revise the narrative you have been working on. Reread your narrative multiple times—checking for mistakes in spelling, punctuation, and capitalization.

Children should revise their narrative. They may write

the revision here or on a separate sheet of paper.

Conventions

Rearrange Sentences Write three sentences that tell a sequence of events out of order. Then exchange sentences with a partner and rearrange his or her sentences.

Children should write the three sentences out of

order. They then exchange sentences with a partner

and put the sentences in the correct sequence.

Children write routinely for a range of tasks, purposes, and audiences. Children practice various conventions of standard English.

Vowel Patterns *aw, au, augh, al*

s<u>aw</u> <u>au</u>to c<u>augh</u>t ch<u>al</u>k

Write a word from the box to match each picture.

daughter draw fall naughty raw sauce thaw walk

1. **walk**	2. **sauce**
3. **draw**	4. **daughter**

Write a word from the box that is the opposite of each word below.

freeze

5. **thaw**

rise

6. **fall**

good

7. **naughty**

cooked

8. **raw**

Mark the space next to the word that has the same vowel sound as *saw.*

9. ■ fault
 □ find
 □ few

10. □ tray
 □ took
 ■ taught

 Children apply grade-level phonics and word analysis skills.

Name _____

DIRECTIONS Write sentences using the words below.

reflected resources

Responses should show contextual understanding

of the words.

Write in
Response to
Reading

DIRECTIONS What is the main idea of the second paragraph on p. 3 of *68 Ways to Save the Planet Before Bedtime?* How does it relate to the main topic of the text? Use evidence from the text to support your answer.

We can save the world. The text says there are 68 ways.

Children demonstrate contextual
understanding of Benchmark Vocabulary.
Children read text closely and use text
evidence in their written answers.

Name _____

DIRECTIONS Revisit the main topics and key details discussed during the lesson. Choose one main topic and key details that you felt were most interesting. Create a chart to help you plan your writing. Then, on a separate sheet of paper, write an opinion about why you thought those key details supported the main topic, and why you found them interesting.

Responses will vary, but children chart one main topic and key details about that topic; then children write why they think their choices are interesting.

Consonant Digraphs Circle the consonant digraphs. Then write a sentence that uses two of the words below.

1. teacher graph think when

2. Responses will vary, but the sentence should use two words listed above.

Children write routinely for a range of tasks, purposes, and audiences. Children practice various conventions of standard English.

Lesson 2

Benchmark Vocabulary

Name _____

DIRECTIONS Write sentences using the words below.

dangerous litter waste

Responses should show contextual understanding of the words.

Write in Response to Reading

DIRECTIONS Reread p. 4 of *68 Ways to Save the Planet Before Bedtime*. How does the graphic on this page help you understand spiders? Use examples from the text to support your answer.

Responses will vary but should use evidence such as the text and graphic showing the importance of spiders to the food chain.

Children demonstrate contextual understanding of Benchmark Vocabulary. Children read text closely and use text evidence in their written answers.

DIRECTIONS Revisit pp. 4–7 of *68 Ways to Save the Planet Before Bedtime.* Select two text features and explain how each one adds to your understanding of the text. Use evidence from the text to support your answer.

Responses will vary but should include how two

text features add to the understanding of the text.

Example: The graphic on p. 4 helps me better

understand what is meant by a food chain; the chart

on p. 6 helps me understand how making a T-shirt

can affect the world.

Children analyze and respond to literary and informational text.

Name _____

DIRECTIONS Think about how *68 Ways to Save the Planet Before Bedtime* connects with the theme and title of the unit, Changing the World. Flag text evidence that shows how the tips in the text can help change the world. Create a Main Purpose Chart to organize your thoughts. Then write a paragraph that explains the connection between the unit title and the text.

Responses will vary but should use text evidence to support the connection.

Conventions

Spelling Patterns—Vowel Digraphs Write two words for each vowel digraph. Responses will vary.

1. ea- Example: seat, reach

2. ee- Example: meet, tree

 Children write routinely for a range of tasks, purposes, and audiences. Children practice various conventions of standard English.

Name _____

DIRECTIONS Write sentences using the words below.

impossible persuade switch completely

Responses should show contextual understanding of

the words.

> **Write in Response to Reading**

DIRECTIONS Reread pp. 8–11 of *68 Ways to Save the Planet Before Bedtime*. What's one connection between global warming and conserving electricity? Use evidence from the text to support your answer.

Responses will vary but could include: When fossil

fuels burn, greenhouse gases are released, which

contributes to global warming.

 Children demonstrate contextual understanding of Benchmark Vocabulary. Children read text closely and use text evidence in their written answers.

Picking Up Sunset Park

Lacey stood at the gate of Sunset Park. What she saw made her want to cry. The storm had knocked down two small trees and scattered branches everywhere.

Her brother, Jared, looked at the mess. "We might as well go home," he said. "It's going to be a while before we can play here again."

"Let's pick up some of the branches," Lacey said.

"That will take all day!" Jared said.

"If we work together, we can get it done quickly," Lacey said.

They began to pick up branches and pile them near the gate. As the pile grew, their friends Marius and Elsa rode by.

"What's going on?" Marius asked.

"The storm blew down some trees," Lacey said. "We're cleaning up."

Marius and Elsa hopped off their bikes and began working. Soon, some neighbors saw the kids at work. They started to help clean up too. Mrs. Cleary came with cold lemonade for everyone. Before long, the branches were all cleared. The adults cut the fallen trees and moved them to the side. The park was almost as good as new. Lacey and Jared happily ran to the swings. They were thrilled. There was even time to play before dinner!

Children read text closely to determine what the text says.

Look for Clues
Underline clues in the story that tell how bad the storm damage was.

Look for Clues: Extend Your Ideas
Circle one way the characters picked up the park.

Ask Questions
Write a question you would ask one of the neighbors who stopped to help. **Responses will vary.**

Example: Why did you stop to help?

Ask Questions: Extend Your Ideas
You are a local newspaper reporter. Write a question you would ask Lacey. **Responses will vary.**

Example: Have you ever done this before?

Make Your Case
On a sheet of paper, tell what the writer wanted to explain. Explain, using examples from the text. **Responses will vary but should use text evidence.**

Make Your Case: Extend Your Ideas
Tell a partner three words you would use to describe Lacey and why. **Responses will vary but might include that she was sensitive because she was sad, she was resourceful because she didn't walk away, and she was convincing because she got her brother to help.**

Children read text closely to determine what the text says.

DIRECTIONS Reread tip 25 on p. 11 of *68 Ways to Save the Planet Before Bedtime*. Then write an opinion paragraph that tells whether or not you agree with the tip. Use a T-chart to list your reasons.

Children should state their opinion and use a T-chart

to list reasons to support the opinion. Example: They

might agree that starting a "no-TV day" is a great

idea because it saves energy and it gives them time

to do other things, such as read books or visit with

family.

Conventions

Spelling Patterns—/g/ or /j/ Cross out the words that do not belong.

1. /g/: ~~biology~~ wagon garden

2. /j/: orange gentle ~~flag~~

Children write routinely for a range of tasks, purposes, and audiences. Children practice various conventions of standard English.

DIRECTIONS Write sentences using the words below.

reduce produce reuse

Responses should show contextual understanding of the words.

> **Write in Response to Reading**

DIRECTIONS Reread p. 12 of *68 Ways to Save the Planet Before Bedtime*. How do the images on this page help to clarify the text? Use specific details and examples to support your answer.

Responses will vary but should use text evidence. The images illustrate the types of garbage that Americans throw away.

Children demonstrate contextual understanding of Benchmark Vocabulary. Children read text closely and use text evidence in their written answers.

DIRECTIONS Reread pp. 14–15. The photographs in this section are meant to help you visualize the sequence for creating a sock monster. Is there anything that you would change or add to this section to improve the explanation? Explain why or why not. Use evidence from the text to support your answer.

Responses will vary but should use text evidence to support the opinion. Example: The photos clearly show each step, so I don't think anything needs to be added.

Children analyze and respond to literary and informational text.

DIRECTIONS Write an opinion paragraph about whether or not you think tips 39–44 on p. 15 of *68 Ways to Save the Planet Before Bedtime* are good ideas. Use linking words to connect your opinions and reasons.

Responses will vary but should use text evidence to support the opinion. Example: I think the ideas are good ones. I really like the idea of making a bag from an old pillowcase because I think it would be cool to decorate it.

Conventions

Spelling Patterns—Diphthongs *oi* **and** *oy* Write two *oi* words and two *oy* words. Responses will vary.

1. *oi:* Example: noise, boil

2. *oy:* Example: joy, royal

Children write routinely for a range of tasks, purposes, and audiences. Children practice various conventions of standard English.

Lesson 5

Name _____

Benchmark Vocabulary

DIRECTIONS Write sentences using the words below.

reason passenger packaging

Responses should show contextual understanding of the words.

Write in Response to Reading

DIRECTIONS Reread pp. 16–17 of *68 Ways to Save the Planet Before Bedtime*. Do you think riding a bike is better for the environment than riding in a car? Use evidence from the text to support your answer.

Responses will vary but should use text evidence including that cars contribute to global warming; bikes do not.

 Children demonstrate contextual understanding of Benchmark Vocabulary. Children read text closely and use text evidence in their written answers.

Unit 6 • Module A • Lesson 5 • 397

Name _____

DIRECTIONS Using evidence from the text, answer the following questions about pp. 16–19 of *68 Ways to Save the Planet Before Bedtime.* Responses will vary. Examples are given.

1. Reread p. 16. What is one benefit of riding a bike?

Riding can help save the world.

2. Reread p. 18. How does using a library contribute to fewer books being made?

If people read the same copy, then fewer copies are needed.

3. Why do you think recycling still contributes to pollution? Use examples from the text to support your answer.

Making recycled paper still produces pollution and adds to global warming.

Children analyze and respond to literary and informational text.

Name _____

DIRECTIONS Review tips 1–58 in *68 Ways to Save the Planet Before Bedtime*. Select two tips that you think are most important for saving the planet, and explain why. Remember to give reasons that support your opinion. Use linking words to connect your opinions and reasons.

Responses will vary, but opinions should be

supported by text evidence. Linking words should be

used to connect the opinions and reasons.

Conventions

Spelling Patterns—Silent *gh* Underline the silent *gh* words. Then write one sentence that uses a silent *gh* word.

1. We caught a fish.

2. The cat climbed high.

3. The sentence should include a silent *gh* word, such as *height*.

Children write routinely for a range of tasks, purposes, and audiences. Children practice various conventions of standard English.

Name _____

Inflected Endings -s, -ed, -ing, -er, -est

Read each word.
Find the base word.
Write the base word on the line.

try + -s = tr**ies** try + -ed = tr**ied** try + -ing = try**ing**

1. hiked	hike	2. skipped	skip	
3. planning	plan	4. shopping	shop	
5. cried	cry	6. liking	like	
7. baking	bake	8. boxes	box	

Find the word that makes sense in the sentences below.
Mark the space to show your answer.

9. Sam is _____ than Luke.

☐ fast
▨ faster
☐ fasting

10. Mia is the _____ person I know.

☐ kinder
☐ kind
▨ kindest

Children apply grade-level phonics and word analysis skills.

Name _____

DIRECTIONS Write sentences using the words below.

selfish sponsored monitor dragging

Responses should show contextual understanding of

the words.

Write in
Response to
Reading

DIRECTIONS Reread p. 22 of *68 Ways to Save the Planet Before Bedtime*. How does the story on this page connect with the main purpose of the text? Use evidence from the text to support your answer.

Responses will vary but should use text evidence

including that things only get better if we think

differently.

Children demonstrate contextual understanding of
Benchmark Vocabulary. Children read text closely
and use text evidence in their written answers.

DIRECTIONS On a separate sheet of paper, list three tips from the book that you would want to share with your friends and family. Be sure to include the title and writer of the book. Then state an opinion about whether or not you thought the book was helpful. Remember to support your opinion with reasons, and to wrap it up with a strong conclusion.

Children list three tips to share, state an opinion with reasons about the book, and conclude with a strong ending.

Conventions

Compound Words Underline the compound word in each sentence. Then write your own sentence using a compound word. Underline the compound word.

1. The firefighter rescued the cat from the tree.

2. She used a flashlight when the lights went out.

3. Responses will vary, but the sentence should

use a compound word, such as *treetop or someone.*

Children write routinely for a range of tasks, purposes, and audiences. Children practice various conventions of standard English.

Lesson 7

Name _____

Benchmark Vocabulary

DIRECTIONS Write a sentence using the word below.

pleaded

Responses should show contextual understanding of the word.

Write in Response to Reading

DIRECTIONS Reread pp. 4–7 of *On Meadowview Street*. What do you learn about Caroline's character in this section? Use details and examples from the text to support your answer.

Responses will vary but should use text evidence

including that she has an appreciation of nature

because she says the flower is beautiful; she didn't

want her dad to mow over the flower.

Children demonstrate contextual understanding of Benchmark Vocabulary. Children read text closely and use text evidence in their written answers.

DIRECTIONS Using evidence from the text, answer the following questions about *On Meadowview Street.*

I. Reread p. 6. What does the response of Caroline's dad tell you about his character?

Responses might include that he doesn't like to do

yard work.

2. Reread pp. 14–15. How do Caroline's parents respond when she tells them that her garden needs a shady spot?

Her parents help her plant a maple tree.

3. Write several sentences about whether or not you admire Caroline and her parents. Do you think most people would take the time to create a meadow in their yard? Use specific examples and details from the text to support your answer. **Responses will vary.**

Example: I admire them because their meadow

became a nature preserve and the neighbors

changed as well.

Children analyze and respond to literary and informational text.

Name _____

DIRECTIONS Revisit *On Meadowview Street* and flag text evidence that helps you understand how Caroline inspired her family, and how her family inspired their neighbors to make changes. Then write an opinion paragraph about how Caroline and her family inspired others. Use linking words to connect opinions and reasons.

Opinion paragraphs might mention that the family

turned their yard into a home for many things by

building birdhouses and ponds. When the neighbors

saw the meadow, they stopped mowing as well.

Conventions

Compound Words Circle the compound words. Then write your own sentence that uses a compound word.

1. (sunflower) neighbor (playground) (lighthouse) flying

2. The sentence has a compound word.

Children write routinely for a range of tasks, purposes, and audiences. Children practice various conventions of standard English.

Name _____

DIRECTIONS Write a sentence using the word below.

unpacked

Responses should show contextual understanding of
the word.

Write in
Response to
Reading

DIRECTIONS Reread pp. 6–7 of *On Meadowview Street*.
How do the words *pleaded* and *raced* affect the story? Use
examples from the text to support your answer.

Responses will vary but should indicate that the

words show Caroline's strong desire to save the

flower. She says, "my flower" when she pleads with

her dad.

Children demonstrate contextual understanding of
Benchmark Vocabulary. Children read text closely
and use text evidence in their written answers.

Name _____

DIRECTIONS Reread pp. 1–13 of *On Meadowview Street.* Write a paragraph about the word choices the author makes. Use examples from the text to show how the author's word choices help you to understand the characters' thoughts, feelings, and actions.

Responses will vary but should point out various words and how they help the reader better understand the characters. Example: Caroline's mother says that a "shady spot sounds nice," which tells us she agrees with Caroline.

Children analyze and respond to literary and informational text.

Name _____

DIRECTIONS Revisit *On Meadowview Street*. Then plan and write a short review that expresses your opinion about the story. Introduce the book, state an opinion about the story, and then support your opinion with reasons. Remember to provide a concluding statement.

Responses will vary, but the book reviews should

introduce the book, state an opinion, include

supporting reasons, and include a concluding

statement.

Conventions

Prefixes Write two sentences that use the prefix *un-*.

1. Both sentences should include one word with

2. the prefix *un-*.

Children write routinely for a range of tasks, purposes, and audiences. Children practice various conventions of standard English.

Lesson 9

Name _____

Benchmark Vocabulary

DIRECTIONS Write a sentence using the word below.

zipping

Responses should show contextual understanding of

the word.

Write in
Response to
Reading

DIRECTIONS Revisit pp. 14–21 of *On Meadowview Street*. Choose one illustration and explain what you learned from it. Use details from the text to support your answer.

Responses will vary. Example: Page 9— Caroline

and her dad build a birdhouse. Both have on safety

glasses, which shows they are careful.

Children demonstrate contextual understanding of Benchmark Vocabulary. Children read text closely and use text evidence in their written answers.

Name _____

DIRECTIONS Think of ways to make your review of *On Meadowview Street* stronger. Then revise and edit your review on a separate sheet of paper. Look for places to add powerful words, and make sure that your ideas are grouped logically. Add linking words to make the connections between opinions and reasons stronger.

Children revise their reviews by adding powerful words and editing for a logical flow. Linking words should be added.

Prefixes Write two of your own sentences that use the prefix *re-*.

1. _Responses will vary, but both sentences should_
 include one word with the prefix re-.

2. _____

Children write routinely for a range of tasks, purposes, and audiences. Children practice various conventions of standard English.

DIRECTIONS Write a sentence using the word below.

shallow

Responses should show contextual understanding of

the word.

> **Write in Response to Reading**

DIRECTIONS Revisit pp. 28–29 of *On Meadowview Street*. How is the structure of this section different from the rest of the text? How does this add to the text? Use examples from the text to support your answer.

There are illustrations and labels. They help us know

the various wildlife and flowers that are part of the

meadow.

Children demonstrate contextual understanding of Benchmark Vocabulary. Children read text closely and use text evidence in their written answers.

DIRECTIONS Revisit pp. 22–31 of *On Meadowview Street*. Write a paragraph that explains how events in the story are directly supported by illustrations. Do you like this type of story structure? Use specific details and examples from the text to support your answer.

Paragraphs should offer specific examples to explain whether children like stories in which the events are directly supported by the illustrations. Example for a positive opinion: On pages 26 and 27, the text says that the neighbors' yards were changing as well. The illustration shows the neighbors planting trees. It also includes a "For Sale" sign on the lawn mower.

Children analyze and respond to literary and informational text.

Name _____

DIRECTIONS Write a paragraph that identifies your opinion about why it is important to take care of Earth. Clearly state your opinion, and list reasons to support that opinion.

Responses will vary, but opinions should be supported with reasons.

Conventions

Root Words Write the root word for each underlined word.

1. I want to be a <u>singer</u>. ___sing___

2. My sister is an <u>artist</u>. ___art___

Children write routinely for a range of tasks, purposes, and audiences. Children practice various conventions of standard English.

Name _____

Abbreviations

Read each abbreviation.
Draw a line to the word it stands for.

1. Ave. Doctor

2. Dr. November

3. Mr. Mister

4. Mon. Avenue

5. Nov. Street

6. St. Monday

Write each abbreviation correctly.

7. apr _____ Apr.

8. mrs _____ Mrs.

9. Mar _____ Mar.

10. fri _____ Fri.

Children apply grade-level phonics and word analysis skills.

DIRECTIONS Write sentences using the words below.

hunters pebble

Responses should show contextual understanding of

the words.

Write in
Response to
Reading

DIRECTIONS Reread "The Lion and the Mouse" and "The Crow and the Pitcher." What is the central message of each fable? Which message do you like most? Use examples to support your answer.

Responses should indicate the central message of

each fable and should include support to explain

which message is preferred.

Children demonstrate contextual understanding of Benchmark Vocabulary. Children read text closely and use text evidence in their written answers.

Name _____

DIRECTIONS Revisit the plan you wrote for your opinion piece about why it is important for people to take care of Earth. Use your plan to draft your opinion piece on a separate sheet of paper. Remember to provide reasons and details that support your opinion. Arrange your reasons and supporting details in a logical order. Use linking words to connect opinions and reasons.

Children draft their opinion pieces, using linking words to arrange the reasons and details in a logical order.

Shades of Meaning Number the words from weakest (1) to strongest (3) in meaning. Then write your own sentence that uses a word with a similar meaning as the word *happy*.

1. freezing __3__ cool __1__ cold __2__

2. angry __2__ furious __3__ mad __1__

3. The sentence uses a synonym for *happy*, such as *joyful*.

Children write routinely for a range of tasks, purposes, and audiences. Children practice various conventions of standard English.

DIRECTIONS Write sentences using the words below.

resources persuade

Responses should show contextual understanding of

the words.

DIRECTIONS Reread pp. 20–21 of *68 Ways to Save the Planet Before Bedtime*. What is one possible connection between the Fast Fact on p. 20 and the main topic of the text? Use examples from the text to support your answer.

Responses will vary but might include that Earth Day

is a reminder that we must save the world.

Children demonstrate contextual understanding of Benchmark Vocabulary. Children read text closely and use text evidence in their written answers.

DIRECTIONS Reread pp. 16–19 of *68 Ways to Save the Planet Before Bedtime*. How does the author use text features to connect concepts in this section? Use specific details and examples from pp. 16–19 to support your answer.

Responses will vary but might include that the text on page 16 is about riding a bike to save the world, and page 17 has seven numbered boxes with additional ways related to travel. Pages 18 and 19 follow the same format, but the topic is about saving paper.

Children analyze and respond to literary and informational text.

Name _____

DIRECTIONS Think of ways to revise your opinion piece from the previous lesson. Add reasons and examples to support your opinions. Add linking words to make stronger connections between opinions, reasons, and ideas. Write your revised opinion piece on a separate sheet of paper.

Children revise their opinion piece and then write the final draft.

Conventions

Shades of Meaning Circle one of the words below. Then write two words that have a similar meaning.

1. happy sad funny said

2. Responses should include two synonyms for the

circled word.

Children write routinely for a range of tasks, purposes, and audiences. Children practice various conventions of standard English.

Name _____

DIRECTIONS Write sentences using the words below.

produce pleaded

Responses should show contextual understanding of

the words.

> Write in
> Response to
> Reading

DIRECTIONS Revisit *68 Ways to Save the Planet Before Bedtime* and *On Meadowview Street*. In what ways are these two texts alike? In what ways are they different? Use examples from both texts to support your answer.

Responses will vary but should use text evidence to

point out at least one way the texts are alike and one

way they are different.

Children demonstrate contextual understanding of Benchmark Vocabulary. Children read text closely and use text evidence in their written answers.

Name _____

Making a Difference, One Bag at a Time

When Annie Wignall was eleven, her mother told her something that made her sad. She said that <u>some children have to leave their homes in hard times. They often must leave everything behind.</u> They lose many things that they love and need. Annie wanted to do something to help. Annie made cute cloth bags for children in need. She found people to donate new items that children might miss from their homes. Annie filled the bags with these things. She put in soap and toothpaste. She found toys to add. She got games and books for the bags. She hoped to give these children lots to make them happy.

Annie started Care Bags Foundation. Every month Annie and other helpers prepare about one hundred Care Bags for Kids. Some people sew the bags. Others give things to put in the bags. Volunteers help fill them. The bags are then given to children in need.*They bring many smiles! Care Bags Foundation also helps children in another way. *It teaches kids how to make a difference. It tells how to start a Care Bags project in their own towns. Care Bags Foundation has made a big difference with each small bag!

Children read text closely to determine what the text says.

Look for Clues

Underline clues. Underline two events that caused something else to happen.

Look for Clues: Extend Your Ideas

Circle ways that people help the Care Bags Foundation.

Ask Questions

Write a question to ask Annie Wignall. **Responses will vary.**

Example: How do you decorate the bags?

Ask Questions: Extend Your Ideas

Write a question that you would ask someone who received a Care Bag. **Responses will vary.**

Example: Why did you leave your home?

Make Your Case

Put a star by the biggest reason that you feel Care Bags Foundation makes a difference.

Two examples are shown.

Make Your Case: Extend Your Ideas

On a sheet of paper, write an opinion about the Care Bags Foundation. Include reasons that support your opinion.

Opinions should include supporting reasons.

Children read text closely to determine what the text says.

DIRECTIONS Read your revised opinion piece several times, checking for a different type of error each time. Use a colored pencil to mark your corrections. Then copy your final, edited opinion piece on the lines below.

Children read and revise their opinion pieces, making edits with colored pencils. Then they copy the final draft.

Conventions

Shades of Meaning In each pair of words, circle the word that has a more positive meaning.

1. (dismissed) rejected

2. (spoke) screamed

Children write routinely for a range of tasks, purposes, and audiences. Children practice various conventions of standard English.

Final Syllables *-tion, -ture, -ion*

Circle a word with *-tion, -ture,* or *-ion* to finish each sentence.

na**tion**

mix**ture**

1,000,000

mill**ion**

1. I saw a horse in the _____.	portion (pasture)
2. I watched from one _____ of the yard.	(section) suction
3. I moved with _____.	culture (caution)
4. I walked in slow _____.	(motion) station
5. I'd like to see a _____ horses.	(million) cushion

Children apply grade-level phonics and word analysis skills.

Lesson 1

Name _____

Benchmark Vocabulary

DIRECTIONS Write sentences using the words below.

liquid ignite

Responses should show contextual understanding of

the words.

Write in
Response to
Reading

DIRECTIONS Write a summary of the author's main purpose for writing *Alfred Nobel: The Man Behind the Peace Prize*. Use evidence from the text to support your answer.

Responses will vary but should include text evidence

that the author's main purpose was to describe how

Alfred's discovery led to the creation of the Nobel

Peace Prize.

Children demonstrate contextual understanding of Benchmark Vocabulary. Children read text closely and use text evidence in their written answers.

DIRECTIONS Identify the author's purpose for writing *Alfred Nobel: The Man Behind the Peace Prize.* Then write a paragraph that explains your opinion about the author's purpose. Use details and examples that support your opinion.

Once children identify the author's purpose, they

write their opinion about the purpose, using text

evidence to support their opinion.

Conventions

Connections Between Words Circle words that have a connection to the word *watermelon.* Then write one sentence using both words.

1. (juicy) shiny (sweet)

2. Responses will vary. The sentence should

include both circled words.

Children write routinely for a range of tasks, purposes, and audiences. Children practice various conventions of standard English.

Name _____

DIRECTIONS Write sentences using the words below.

startled ports

Responses should show contextual understanding of

the words.

> **Write in Response to Reading**

DIRECTIONS Reread the first paragraph on p. 126 of _Alfred Nobel: The Man Behind the Peace Prize_. What is the main topic of this paragraph? Use examples from the text to support your answer.

Responses should include text evidence about how

the useful liquid can blast away rock and help make

safer weapons.

Children demonstrate contextual understanding of Benchmark Vocabulary. Children read text closely and use text evidence in their written answers.

Name _____

DIRECTIONS Revisit pp. 124–131 of *Alfred Nobel: The Man Behind the Peace Prize.* Do you think Alfred Nobel wanted to make the world safer? Explain why or why not. Use details and examples from the text to support your answer.

Responses will vary. Example: Yes. The text says that Alfred, with his family's help, experimented day and night to try different ways to safely ignite nitroglycerin.

Children analyze and respond to literary and informational text.

Name _____

DIRECTIONS Write about how the topic of *Alfred Nobel: The Man Behind the Peace Prize* connects with the unit title, Changing the World. Use words from the text to support your response.

Responses will vary. Example: The text says that

nitroglycerin changed the way roads, bridges, and

towns were built, which fits with the unit title.

Conventions

Connections Between Words Write two sentences that use connected words.

1. _Responses will vary. Both sentences use a set_

of related or connecting words. Example: Alfred

2. _experimented with ways to make the mixture_

safe. He tested and tested until he got it right.

Children write routinely for a range of tasks, purposes, and audiences. Children practice various conventions of standard English.

Lesson 3

Name _____

DIRECTIONS Write sentences using the words below.

invention dynamite prevent

Responses should show contextual understanding of

the words.

DIRECTIONS Reread p. 141 of *Alfred Nobel: The Man Behind the Peace Prize*. Why did Alfred believe that his invention would prevent war? Use examples from the text to support your answer.

The text says that Alfred thought that if people were

afraid of the harm that explosions could cause,

perhaps they would settle things peacefully.

Children demonstrate contextual understanding of Benchmark Vocabulary. Children read text closely and use text evidence in their written answers.

Name _____

DIRECTIONS Think about how Alfred reacted to the loss of Emil by continuing to work on making nitroglycerin safe. Write an opinion about how Alfred proceeded after the tragedy. Would you have done the same thing? Explain why or why not.

Responses will vary, but opinions should be

supported by reasons.

Conventions

Connections Between Words Tell how the underlined words are connected. Then write a sentence, using connected words.

1. Today we had tacos for lunch. The <u>meat</u> is <u>spicy</u>, and the <u>tomatoes</u> are <u>juicy</u>. Responses will vary.

 Example: The words tell more details about the lunch.

2. Sentence should use words that have a connection.

Children write routinely for a range of tasks, purposes, and audiences. Children practice various conventions of standard English.

Name _____

DIRECTIONS Write sentences using the words below.

will estate

Responses should show contextual understanding of

the words.

Write in
Response to
Reading

DIRECTIONS Reread pp. 142–149 of *Alfred Nobel: The Man Behind the Peace Prize*. Do you think Alfred would have created The Nobel Prizes if he had not read his obituary? Use evidence from the text to support your answer.

Responses will vary. Example: No. It was only when

he read his own obituary that he realized that others

saw him as a man who became wealthy by inventing

ways to kill.

Children demonstrate contextual understanding of Benchmark Vocabulary. Children read text closely and use text evidence in their written answers.

Name _____

DIRECTIONS Draft a letter to the editor in response to the editorial that your class wrote. Decide whether you agree or disagree with the opinion presented in the editorial. Include reasons to support your opinion.

Responses will vary. The opinion should be supported

by reasons.

Conventions

Connections Between Words Write sentences using the words below. Then briefly explain the connection between the words.

Alfred Nobel life inspirational famous

Responses will vary. Example: Alfred Nobel became

famous in life for rewarding inspirational deeds.

Children write routinely for a range of tasks, purposes, and audiences. Children practice various conventions of standard English.

Benchmark Vocabulary

DIRECTIONS Write sentences using the words below.

terribly escape

Responses should show contextual understanding of

the words.

Write in Response to Reading

DIRECTIONS Reread pp. 150–151 of *Alfred Nobel: The Man Behind the Peace Prize*. How do you think Alfred would feel about the list of Nobel Peace Prize winners? Use details from the text to support your answer.

Responses will vary, but opinions should be

supported by text evidence. Example: Alfred would

be proud. He didn't want to be remembered as a man

who was responsible for an invention that kills.

 Children demonstrate contextual understanding of Benchmark Vocabulary. Children read text closely and use text evidence in their written answers.

Name _____

DIRECTIONS Revisit *Alfred Nobel: The Man Behind the Peace Prize* and select one cause-and-effect relationship. Then write a paragraph that explains what happened and why. Use specific details from the text to support your answer.

Responses will vary. Example: Alfred and his brother made and sold nitroglycerin in Sweden. As a result, it was used to build roads and railways, bridges, ports, and towns.

Children analyze and respond to literary and informational text.

Name _____

DIRECTIONS Write a paragraph that expresses an opinion about how Alfred's invention impacted communities. Use linking words and phrases to connect your opinions and reasons. Remember to clearly state your opinion at the beginning of your paragraph.

Responses will vary, but opinions should be

clearly stated in the opening paragraph, should be

supported by reasons, and should use linking words.

Conventions

Connections Between Words Write two sentences that use words connected with the word *legacy*.

Responses will vary. Example: After Nobel died, his

entire estate was used to create the Nobel Prizes.

That is Nobel's legacy.

 Children write routinely for a range of tasks, purposes, and audiences. Children practice various conventions of standard English.

Name _____

Suffixes *-ness, -less, -able, -ible*

Add *-ness, -less, -able,* or *-ible* to each word to make a word from the box.
Write the new word on the line.

affordable	fearless	fitness	goodness
reversible	terrible	thankless	useless

1. afford **affordable**

2. fit **fitness**

3. thank **thankless**

4. fear **fearless**

5. good **goodness**

6. use **useless**

Pick a word from the box to match the clue.
Write the word on the line.

7. has two sides you can use: **reversible**

8. very bad, something feared: **terrible**

Children apply grade-level phonics and word analysis skills.

Name _____

DIRECTIONS Write sentences using the words below.

accomplishment legacy

Responses should show contextual understanding of

the words.

Write in Response to Reading

DIRECTIONS Reread pp. 148–151 of *Alfred Nobel: The Man Behind the Peace Prize*. How do the text features in this section connect with Alfred's dream of making the world safer for people? Use details from the text to support your answer.

Responses will vary but might include that the art

shows what the medal looks like, and the pages list

who won the Peace Prize.

Children demonstrate contextual understanding of Benchmark Vocabulary. Children read text closely and use text evidence in their written answers.

Name _____

DIRECTIONS Reread pp. 146–148 of *Alfred Nobel: The Man Behind the Peace Prize*. Write an opinion about Alfred Nobel's will from the point of view of one of his family members. Use persuasive words to support your opinion. Remember to provide a strong concluding statement.

Responses will vary, but opinions should be from the

viewpoint of a relative, include persuasive words,

and have a concluding statement.

Conventions

Use Root Words to Identify Unknown Words Write sentences using words with the root words *sleep* and *develop*.

1. Responses will vary. Examples: *sleepless, development*

2. _____

Children write routinely for a range of tasks, purposes, and audiences. Children practice various conventions of standard English.

DIRECTIONS Write sentences using the words below.

awkward serious

Responses will vary but should show contextual

understanding of the words.

Write in
Response to
Reading

DIRECTIONS Reread pp. 173–175 of *A Picture Book of Eleanor Roosevelt*. How does the information in this section relate to the main purpose of the text? Use details from the text to support your answer.

Responses will vary but might include that the

information tells more about Eleanor. She didn't wait

to do things, and she followed her heart.

Children demonstrate contextual understanding of Benchmark Vocabulary. Children read text closely and use text evidence in their written answers.

Name _____

DIRECTIONS Identify the author's purpose for writing about Eleanor Roosevelt. Then list four pieces of evidence from the text that support the author's purpose.

Author's Purpose: <u>The author's purpose was to write a biography about Eleanor Roosevelt.</u>

Text Evidence: <u>Responses will vary but should include any four facts that the author wrote about Eleanor Roosevelt.</u>

Children analyze and respond to literary and informational text.

(See below)

Lesson 7

Name _____

Writing

DIRECTIONS Write a paragraph that gives Eleanor Roosevelt a new honorary title. Revisit the text for ideas. Remember to support your choice with strong reasons from the text, and explain why you believe she deserves the new title.

Responses will vary. Accept any title that is supported by strong reasons.

Conventions

Use Root Words to Identify Unknown Words Write sentences using words with the root words *invent* and *command*.

1. Responses will vary. Sentences should include forms of the words *invent* and *command.*

2.

Children write routinely for a range of tasks, purposes, and audiences. Children practice various conventions of standard English.

442 • Unit 6 • Module B • Lesson 7

DIRECTIONS Write a sentence using the word below.

pure

Responses should show contextual understanding of

the word.

DIRECTIONS Reread p. 156 of *A Picture Book of Eleanor Roosevelt*. What reasons does the author provide to support the claim that Eleanor missed her father terribly? Use evidence from the text to support your answer.

The text says, "Eleanor missed him terribly and

dreamed of him often."

Children demonstrate contextual understanding of Benchmark Vocabulary. Children read text closely and use text evidence in their written answers.

Name _____

Wanted: Great Student Leaders!

Do you have lots of school spirit and fun ideas for helping your school? Are you a good leader? Then you may belong on the student council!

Many schools have student councils. <u>These are groups of students who are chosen to share ideas and make decisions about student activities.</u> Students often elect student council members in a class or grade-level election. Council members work hard to be good students, good citizens, and good examples to everyone at school.

Some students are officers with special duties. They lead the council meetings, keep records, and work with school staff members. Others are representatives. They talk to the students in their classes to get ideas. Later, they report back to the class about decisions the student council has made.

*But what does a student council actually do? It might organize an event, such as a school carnival. It might raise money for new equipment. It might plan volunteer activities, such as a food drive, to help people in the community. If there is a problem in the school, the student council may discuss possible solutions to the problem.

Are you ready to make a difference in your school? If so, the student council may be the place for you!

Children read text closely to determine what the text says.

Name _____

Look for Clues
Underline text clues that help you understand what a student council does.

Look for Clues: Extend Your Ideas
Circle what council members work hard at.

Ask Questions
Write a question that you might ask students that are on a student council. **Responses will vary.**

How often does the council meet?

Ask Questions: Extend Your Ideas
Write a question to ask of a student running for student council. **Responses will vary.**

Why do you want to be elected?

Make Your Case
Put a star above a sentence that helps you understand the author's main purpose.

Responses will vary.

Make Your Case: Extend Your Ideas
On a sheet of paper, list two personality traits you think a student council member should have.

Responses will vary. Example: honesty and integrity

 Children read text closely to determine what the text says.

DIRECTIONS Write a list of facts from the text that support Eleanor's opinion that boarding school was a good place. Remember to only include facts from her life that support why she felt that way.

At her grandmother's house, Eleanor had many rules
to follow. The servant screamed at her and pulled her
hair. However, at school, the teachers and students
thought she was wonderful.

Conventions

Identify Root Words Write a sentence using the root word for each word shown below.

difference discovery accomplishment

I. Responses will vary, but the sentences should
include the words *differ, discover,* and *accomplish.*

Children write routinely for a range of tasks, purposes, and audiences. Children practice various conventions of standard English.

Name _____

DIRECTIONS Write a sentence using the word below.

stricken

Responses should show contextual understanding of

the word.

DIRECTIONS Reread the second paragraph on p. 161 of *A Picture Book of Eleanor Roosevelt*. How does the word *hated* impact the text? Use examples from the text to support your answer.

Responses will vary but should include that the word

conveys just how much Eleanor disliked the parties.

Children demonstrate contextual understanding of Benchmark Vocabulary. Children read text closely and use text evidence in their written answers.

DIRECTIONS Using evidence from the text, answer the following questions about *A Picture Book of Eleanor Roosevelt*.

1. Reread p. 165. Describe how the phrase "paid little attention" impacts the text? **Responses will vary.**

The phrase implies that the guests weren't

interested in the couple.

2. Reread p. 167. What does the word *refused* tell you about Eleanor Roosevelt? **Responses will vary.**

Eleanor had a mind of her own and would not be

bossed around.

3. Reread pp. 168–169. List several words and phrases from this section that help to explain Eleanor Roosevelt's importance to Franklin Delano Roosevelt.

Responses will vary but might include *his nurse,*

traveled for him, **and** *brought back detailed reports.*

Children analyze and respond to literary and informational text.

Name _____

DIRECTIONS Why do you think the author chose to write about Eleanor Roosevelt? Revisit *A Picture Book of Eleanor Roosevelt* to look for clues about the author's purpose. Then develop a plan for your opinion paragraph.

Children look for clues to develop a plan for their

opinion about the author's purpose, which is to write

a biography of Eleanor Roosevelt.

Identify and Use the Prefix *re-* Write sentences using words with the prefix *re-*.

1. Responses will vary. Both sentences should use

 words with the prefix. Examples include: *react,*

2. *rebuy, reappear, rebraid,* and *rejoin.*

Children write routinely for a range of tasks, purposes, and audiences. Children practice various conventions of standard English.

DIRECTIONS Write sentences using the words below.

rights minorities

Responses should show contextual understanding of

the words.

Write in
Response to
Reading

DIRECTIONS Reread pp. 172–176 of *A Picture Book of Eleanor Roosevelt*. What key ideas and details support the idea that Eleanor Roosevelt was "First Lady of the World." Use evidence from the text to support your answer.

Responses will vary but should include that Eleanor

spoke out for all people and that she traveled the

world to visit soldiers.

Children demonstrate contextual understanding of Benchmark Vocabulary. Children read text closely and use text evidence in their written answers.

DIRECTIONS Write a paragraph that explains a connection between Eleanor Roosevelt's actions and one of the historical events listed on the time line on p. 182. Use evidence from the text to show the connection.

Responses will vary but should connect an action to an event on the time line. Example: Eleanor wanted to ensure peace. As the UN representative, she met with world leaders to discuss their differences. She said, "If we are to live together, we have to talk."

Children analyze and respond to literary and informational text.

Name _____

DIRECTIONS Write a draft of your opinion piece about why you think the author chose to write about Eleanor Roosevelt. Revisit *A Picture Book of Eleanor Roosevelt* to look for clues about the author's opinion. Use your list of key ideas and details from the previous lesson to support your writing.

Responses will vary, but opinions should include the

key ideas and details from the child's list.

Conventions

Dictionaries Reread pp. 172–182 of *A Picture Book of Eleanor Roosevelt*. Find one unfamiliar word and look it up in a dictionary. Then write a sentence using the word.

Responses will vary but should include a sentence in

which an unfamiliar word is used correctly.

Children write routinely for a range of tasks, purposes, and audiences. Children practice various conventions of standard English.

Name _____

Prefixes *micro-, mid-, mis-, non-*

Read the clues.

Write micro-, mid-, mis-, or **non-** to finish the words.

microscope **mid**air

misplace **non**fat

1. middle of the week **mid** _____ week	**2.** an error **mis** _____ take
3. true story **non** _____ fiction	**4.** act badly **mis** _____ behave
5. peaceful **non** _____ violent	**6.** about July 1 **mid** _____ year
7. an error in printing **mis** _____ print	**8.** something that makes sound louder **micro** _____ phone
9. makes no sense **non** _____ sense	**10.** a wrong act **mis** _____ deed

Children apply grade-level phonics and word analysis skills.

Name _____

DIRECTIONS Write sentences using the words below.

invention stricken

Responses should show contextual understanding of

the words.

> **Write in Response to Reading**

DIRECTIONS Revisit *Alfred Nobel: The Man Behind the Peace Prize* and *A Picture Book of Eleanor Roosevelt*. What did Eleanor Roosevelt and Alfred Nobel have in common? Use details from both texts to support your answer.

Responses will vary. Example: Children might use

text evidence to show that both Alfred and Eleanor

cared about people.

Children demonstrate contextual understanding of Benchmark Vocabulary. Children read text closely and use text evidence in their written answers.

Name _____

DIRECTIONS Think of ways to make your opinion piece about Eleanor Roosevelt stronger. Add reasons and examples to support your opinions. Revise your conclusion to make it stronger. Revisit the text to look for additional reasons and examples.

Responses will vary but should include reasons and

examples to support the opinions.

Conventions

Use Dictionaries Revisit _A Picture Book of Eleanor Roosevelt_ to find two words you do not know. Use a dictionary to find the meaning of each word.

1. _Responses will vary but should include two_

2. _unfamiliar words and definitions._

Children write routinely for a range of tasks, purposes, and audiences. Children practice various conventions of standard English.

Benchmark Vocabulary

DIRECTIONS Write sentences using the words below.

legacy pure

Responses should show contextual understanding of

the words.

Write in
Response to
Reading

DIRECTIONS Revisit p. 148 of *Alfred Nobel: The Man Behind the Peace Prize* and p. 178 of *A Picture Book of Eleanor Roosevelt*. What do these sections tell you about how Alfred and Eleanor felt about world peace? Use examples from both texts to support your answer.

Responses will vary but should include that Alfred's

legacy was the Peace Prize and that Eleanor worked

to ensure peace.

Children demonstrate contextual understanding of Benchmark Vocabulary. Children read text closely and use text evidence in their written answers.

Name _____

DIRECTIONS Write a paragraph about historical events that happened in both Alfred Nobel's and Eleanor Roosevelt's lives that showed why they worked toward world peace. Use examples from both texts to support your answer.

Responses will vary. Example: Alfred's false death notice prompted Alfred to use his wealth to fund the Nobel Prizes. Eleanor lived during the Second World War. After the war, she said she wanted to ensure peace and worked at the United Nations toward that end.

Children analyze and respond to literary and informational text.

Name _____

Writing

DIRECTIONS Exchange your draft with a partner. Read your partner's draft several times, and use a colored pencil to make it easy to see what has been marked. Then reread your own draft. Use a dictionary to check the spelling of any words that your partner circled. Edit your revised draft using the checklist your class prepared. Make notes as needed.

Children use colored pencils to edit their partners'

drafts. Each child then edits his or her draft, using

the checklist prepared by the class.

Conventions

Use Dictionaries List three words from your opinion draft that you were unsure how to spell. Use a dictionary to check the spelling, and then write sentences using those words.

Responses will vary but should include sentences

using the three words.

Children write routinely for a range of tasks, purposes, and audiences. Children practice various conventions of standard English.